Buteyko
Meets
Dr Mew

Patrick McKeown

ButeykoClinic.com
ButeykoKids.com

Patrick McKeown
ButeykoClinic.com
Imprint of Asthma Care
Buteyko meets Dr Mew
Published by: ButeykoClinic.com
Imprint of Asthma Care
ISBN: 978-0956682307
Loughwell, Moycullen, Co Galway

Web: www.ButeykoClinic.com
Email: info@buteykoclinic.com
© Patrick McKeown 2010

Illustrations by Rebecca Burgess

Be who you are and say what you feel, because those who mind don't matter and those who matter don't mind.

— Dr. Seuss

Table of Contents

Book One—Especially for Teens 1

Meet Dr Mew 2
Grow the Perfect Face 6
Who Wants Crooked Teeth? 8
Unblock the Nose 10
Tiger the Cat 15
Good Sports Performance 19
Oxygenate Your Brain 22
Don't Look Dumb 25
Look Good, Feel Good 28

Book Two—Especially for Parents 30

What Is Good Breathing? 31
Who is Dr Buteyko? 34
Overbreathing 35
How to Recognise Habitual Overbreathing 36
How Should We Breathe? 37
Carbon Dioxide 38
Bohr Effect Simply Explained 40
Improve Oxygenation 42
Symptoms of Chronic Hyperventilation 43
How Might it Apply to Your Child? 44
Growing the Perfect Face 47
Who is Dr Mew? 49

Dr Mew's patients 50

Evolution of Crooked Teeth 53

Diet and Mouth Breathing 54

The Big Teethed Mule 56

Mouth Breathing Causes Crooked Teeth 57

Every Child has the Potential to Grow an Attractive Face 58

How Children Develop Crooked Teeth 60

Craniofacial Abnormalities 66

Reversible at an Early Age 69

Orthodontics: Choose Wisely 71

Identical Twins 73

Sixty Minutes TV Interview 75

Everything To Correct Breathing 80

Note of Caution 81

Unblock the Nose 83

Step It Up! 86

Reduced Breathing 90

Approach One – Blocking One Nostril 92

Approach Two—Hand Over Face 94

Approach Three – Ryan Hides His Breathing 96

Correct Tongue Posture 98

Correct Swallow 101

How to Stop Cough and Wheeze 103

Lifestyle 107

Snoring and Sleep Apnoea 108

Mouth Breathing and Diet 114

Especially For Infants 116

What to do Going Forward 122

Conclusion..125

Appendices & References.......................131

Book Three—Especially for Children ...137

Meet Michael... 138
Summer sports Day in Tumbletown.. 139
Michael meets Argo the wizard 140
ABC Game... 141
How to unblock your nose.. 143
What is our nose for? 144
Argo lets Michael in on a secret... 145
Finding the correct "spot"... 147
Walk the steps 150
What causes wheezing and coughing.. 153
Avoiding triggers 155
The secret to breathe correctly.. 156
The big race.. 157
The Winner.. 161
My Step Diary 165

Foreword

As a small child I was constantly berated if I did not 'Stand up Straight' and 'Keep My Mouth Shut' and at school the headmaster had a plywood cut out of a camel which was pointed at any child who sat with their back bent. Nowadays few children suffer this ignominy but the ratio of four year olds that spend the majority of the time with their mouths open, exceeds eighty percent.

Few parents realise the true extent that their child's health can be damaged by such simple factors. As a surgeon it used to upset me to realise that just for the lack of this knowledge many attractive kids would grow up with plain faces and chronic health problems.

Patrick McKeown is doing his best to redress this in his colourful and tactful way and I would like to give him every encouragement. My orthodontic education was both strict and restrictive; extractions were considered inevitable and the possibilities of changing the growth of the face very limited. It was many years later that I discovered that much can be done by both treatment and especially persuasion to encourage children to create their own future.

Dr John Mew, orthodontist

BOOK ONE

ESPECIALLY FOR TEENS

ButeykoTeens Learn the Secret

That's right Dr. Mew. We remember visiting you too.

And do you remember the little chat we had at the time?

Yes we do...

You told us how important it is to breathe through our noses...

..And keep our tongues up in the roof of the mouth, so that its tip is resting gently behind but not touching the top front teeth.

That's right. And I see that you listened very well. Lauren, you kept your mouth closed...

You can??

...and I can tell because your face has grown well. So I know that you breathe only through your nose.

And why should we keep our mouths closed?

That's right. Aoife, when our mouth is open our face grows downwards.

Because when our mouth is closed and our tongue is resting on the roof of our mouth, our face grows nicely and we grow up to be good-looking.

Our cheeks sink. Our nose looks bigger. Our faces become narrow, our teeth are crooked and we have no chin.

The lower half of your face is determined by where you place your tongue.

But Dr. Mew, I kept my mouth open and was able to place my tongue in the roof of my mouth.

Ha ha, I have heard that one before.

Try it now, Aoife.

That's what I thought.

When your mouth is closed, your tongue exerts pressure to shape your top jaw and teeth.

 V shaped

 U shaped

It's also very important to swallow correctly. Fine, healthy jaws with straight teeth are 'U' shaped.

The most accomplished men and women have fine, strong jaws and teeth.

Think of your favourite movie star or performer.

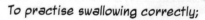

To practise swallowing correctly;

For this exercise, you need an ice cream wafer. Break off a piece about the size of a quarter, 10p or a one euro coin.

Chew until you can make a ball out of it. Hollow your tongue and position the ball near the front.

Place the tip of your tongue on the 'N' spot and close your teeth pressing your tongue firmly against the skin of the roof of your mouth and not the teeth.

Then swallow, sucking at the same time. The teeth should bite together, the lips should be held apart in a big grin.

This helps the back of the tongue rise up and stops the lips being involved in the swallow. An adult can also check how you did. With a correct swallow there is no movement from the outside of your face.

Use a mirror afterwards to see that none of the ice cream wafer is left on your tongue. If you don't have a wafer, you can use a small piece of bread.

From now on, every time you swallow make sure that your tongue is in the roof of the mouth.

Aoife, look at your sisters top jaw.

See, Laurens top jaw is shaped like a 'U' and her teeth are straight.

The only difference between the two of you is that Lauren closed her mouth and you didn't.

And another thing, mouth breathers often have dry mouths.

A dry mouth is a breeding ground for bacteria and plaque, which cause dental cavities and gum disease, and bad breath...

...which can scare off your friends or any of the boys that you may be interested in.

Dr. Mew, I had a very blocked nose. I was able to unblock it and breathe through it easily.

I also find that my performance in sports has improved. I don't get out of breath.

When I was breathing through my mouth, I was always out of breath.

Aoife is always out of breath and now I perform much better than she does.

Heheh...

Well, Patrick is here today. I am sure that he will ask you to do breathing exercises.

Hi Lauren, hi Aoife. Today we are going to practice some exercises to correct your breathing.

When we last met, I showed you an exercise to unblock your nose. It's a simple exercise. Can you remember it?

Yes, this is what I do ...

Take a gentle breath in through my nose. If my nose is totally blocked. Then I take a tiny breath through the corner of my mouth.

Gently breathe out through my nose.

Pinch my nose with fingers to hold my breath.

Sway my body or gently move my head up and down to distract myself; Sometimes I also walk around while holding my breath.

Pretend that I am
underwater and hold
my breath for as long
as possible.

When I can no longer
hold my breath,
I let go of my nose
and breathe through it.

Then I calm my breathing
immediately.

And then I drop my
shoulders and relax.

And does it work?

Yes, of course, but sometimes I have to do it a few times.

When my nose is really blocked, I repeat the exercise every minute for five or six times.

I also find that when I do well with my steps exercise, my nose is free, my cough is gone, I have more energy and can breathe through my nose.

When my steps exercise is low, I often feel that I don't get enough air when I breathe through my nose.

When your steps are low, you are breathing too much air into your body.

You might also feel that you are not getting enough air when you close your mouth.

This is not because your nose is too narrow. It is because your breathing volume is too large. Your breathing is noisy, heavy and loud.

Aoife, can you remember how to do the steps exercise?

Yes I can but they are not very high.

Of course. They are not high. That is because you have not been practicing them.

When your steps are high, your breathing is being corrected and it is easy to breathe through your nose.

You have also been breathing with your mouth open.

I never understand when a youngster does not keep his or her mouth closed since doing so has a huge impact on our looks, health and energy levels. Who does not want a perfect face?

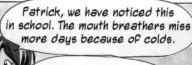
Patrick, we have noticed this in school. The mouth breathers miss more days because of colds.

I will tell you a story about tiger the cat.

Tiger loves to keep himself clean.

He licks his fur all day long.

When his spit dries, it breaks into tiny pieces and floats into the air.

Little Johnny walks by with his mouth open and sucks tiger's spit into his mouth.

If little Johnny knew what was in the air, he would be sure to keep his mouth closed!

Aoife, is that a good enough reason for you to close your mouth? Will you show me how you do your steps?

Hhm...

I close my mouth and breathe only through my nose.

I breathe out gently.

I then pinch my nose with my fingers to hold my breath on the out-breath.

I walk as many steps as possible.

When I feel a strong need to breathe, I release my fingers from my nose and breathe through my nose.

I then calm my breathing in two or so breaths.

I have someone count aloud every ten steps for feedback.

I don't get stressed.

Aoife, I counted your steps. You were able to take 25. Shall I try?

I'm not at all happy with that number. Yes, try it, Lauren.

1...2...3...4...

...83...84...

Wow... 85!

Remember that if you take less than sixty steps, all of your symptoms will be present every day. You may experience poor sleep. A blocked nose, wheezing, poor concentration, mouth breathing and perform inadequately in sports. In addition, your brainpower will not be as strong as it should be.

The goal is eighty steps. I did take eighty steps but when I stopped practising, that number dropped.

I found that I could no longer play football and my nose was constantly blocked.

How would a low number of steps affect performance in sports?

Lauren, that is a good question.

Two boys from Dunboyne know the answer to that.

The first boy, Muller, swims underwater and is able to take four strokes before he needs to come up for air.

The second boy, Fergal, swims the entire length of the 25-meter pool on one breath. Now who do you think is the fitter of the two?

Surely Fergal is. he could go farther on one breath.

Yes, he could. He is more efficient. He performs better than Muller. And who do you think has higher steps?

It must be Fergal, as he can hold his breath longer.

An American Hummer drives ten miles to the gallon, while an efficient car like a Diesel BMW drives 50 miles to the gallon. Efficiency also affects humans. It is all about the amount of air that we need to walk or run a distance.

Exactly Aoife. Just like a car.

People who breathe efficiently can do so much more with each breath.

Patrick, it's not just about taking steps to be efficient, our breathing should be quiet and calm all the time.

Our mouths should be closed and we should not see or hear our breathing.

And how do you do that?

I watch and feel my breathing.

I ask myself while I'm on the way to school, in school,

doing my homework, watching TV and meeting friends if I am breathing too much.

When you breathe quietly, your blood vessels open and greater volumes of oxygen are released to your organs and systems. The brain receives more oxygen. Teenagers who breathe through their mouths are sending less oxygen to their brain.

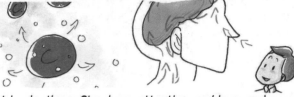

That is why they often have attention problems and poor concentration. They are half asleep while going about.

You also said that sick people breathe heavily. You can hear and see their breathing. I was in an old age home and I could see and hear most of them breathing.

Aoife, the sicker the person, the more noisy his or her breathing is during rest.

You don't want people thinking you are older than you are because you breathe noisily, do you?

I-I'm not that bad!

I also practice reducing my breathing. I allow my breathing to quiet by telling it to calm down, relax and go quiet. I know that I am doing this correctly when I feel the need for air.

Okay, maybe I am.

So what is this feeling of a need for air?

I make my breathing so quiet, as if I have no movement from the neck downwards.

I only take a tiny amount of air into my nose. Because I am breathing less air than what I usually do, I feel slightly breathless.

And do you feel warmer?

Yes, I do.

Why do you think you get warmer when you breathe less?

I feel like I am going for a walk. In fact, it is just like being in a training session. I do this for three minutes at a time. I keep telling my breathing to relax, which works. My breathing goes quiet and I feel a hunger for air.

You already said that when we breathe less, our blood vessels open. Is this the reason?

Yes, absolutely. Quiet breathing in and out of the nose opens up the blood vessels and delivers more oxygen throughout the body.

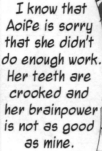

I know that Aoife is sorry that she didn't do enough work. Her teeth are crooked and her brainpower is not as good as mine.

I am so glad that I have been doing the work. I feel so much better as a result.

So Lauren, what do you do each day?

I do two lines of six steps each day. It takes about five minutes per line.

Well Patrick,

I also watch my breathing many times throughout the day, and of course I keep my mouth closed with my tongue in the roof of my mouth.

I also keep my mouth closed at night. I use the paper tape that you told me about.

Patrick, I'm going to start doing the steps from now on.

I'm also going to keep my mouth closed and keep my tongue in the roof of my mouth.

When I watched a few films, every dumb character had his or her mouth open.

So what they are saying is that only dumb people go about with their mouths open.

Ha ha. And in films, they try to base characters on real life.

You never see an intelligent person with his or her mouth open.

That is true to life. When you breathe through your mouth, less oxygen goes to your brain.

As a result, your brainpower is reduced.

I see.

This makes sense, as how can you be intelligent when your brain is receiving less oxygen?

Dr. Mew, you know my neighbour David, whom you saw as a little boy.

Aoife, I remember David very well. He had a fine face as a young boy, with high cheekbones, a good strong jaw and straight teeth.

Here is a photo of him.

He got a gerbil as a present when he was fourteen years old. This blocked his nose, so he started to breathe through his mouth. Here is a photo of him now.

Do you think his face looks well?

No, not at all. He does not have a handsome face. He should have kept his mouth closed. He has no chin.

His nose is too big and his eyes don't look right. Does this happen to every teenager who breathes through his or her mouth?

Yes, it does indeed, with slight variations from teenager to teenager. But this is not just about his looks;

His mother tells me that he snores at night and he is too tired during the day to do anything. This is quite unfortunate at such a young age.

So girls, have you a message to tell the readers?

Yes. Follow four simple steps for a wonderful life:

1. Keep your mouth closed all the time.

2. Place three quarters of your tongue in the roof of your mouth, with its tip resting behind (but not touching) your top front teeth.

3. Practise two lines of steps each day, six repetitions of steps per line.

4. Breathe quietly all day long.

That is the great secret to a wonderful life!

Steps Record

Date	My Steps	One Minute Rest	My Steps	One Minute Rest	My Steps	One Minute Rest	My Steps	One Minute Rest	My Steps	One Minute Rest	My Steps

Photocopy this page and start recording your progress. Rest for one minute between each repetition of steps. Two rows of steps per day with at least two hours rest in between each line. Steps should be practised on an empty tummy.

BOOK TWO

ESPECIALLY FOR PARENTS

WHAT IS GOOD
BREATHING?

Ancient Chinese philosopher Lao Tzu once said that "The perfect man breathes as if he does not breathe." In order to live, the three ingredients of water, food and air are vital but which is more important?

We can live without food for weeks, and without water for days but we can live without air for just a few moments. If we measure the importance of each element by how long we can live without it, air becomes so much more important than either food or water.

We all know the importance of good air quality. Smog, pollution or inferior air has a negative impact to our health. But what about the quantity of air? It is not common knowledge but breathing a large volume of air can also be detrimental to our health.

Silence is a sign of good breathing, i.e. when the mouth is closed and our air exchange (breathing in and out) is silent during a period of rest. Good breathing is regular and calm without sighs or sniffs. Good breathing is when we cannot see or hear it. It is unnoticeable. This is what Lao Tzu meant when he said "the perfect man breathes as if he does not breathe." When the body is efficient, breathing is quiet.

On the other hand, inefficient breathing is noisy, heavy, loud, and erratic. It takes effort, but breathing should not be an effort. When breathing is done through the mouth more air is taken in but less oxygen is delivered throughout the body. This might be counter to what you believe, but when you understand how oxygen is delivered from the blood it will make sense. Pale faces, black circles under the eyes, stuffy noses, asthma, snoring, behavioural problems, poor concentration, craniofacial abnormalities are all significantly affected by poor breathing habits.

Each year, I see the breathing habits of children and teenagers throughout Europe and the USA. Many attend my courses because they are wheezing or coughing. Others come for help with sports, to improve their performance and fitness. Others come because they have been referred by their dentist who is only too aware of the problems associated with mouth breathing.

They all have one thing in common—they have learned the bad habit of heavy breathing.

Their breathing is often through the mouth and is noisy with regular sighs and yawns. But the good news is that it can be easily addressed as soon as the child or teenager is aware of it. All it takes is a little commitment and discipline. The rewards are a better looking child with correct craniofacial development and better health. Incorporating the work of Dr Buteyko and Dr Mew is instrumental to improving every child and teenagers health.

WHO IS DR BUTEYKO?

The Buteyko Method was developed in the 1950's by Russian doctor Konstantin Buteyko. His method has been practised by hundreds of thousands of children and adults for a variety of conditions including mouth breathing, hay fever, blocked nose, snoring, sleep apnoea, asthma, high blood pressure, anxiety, stress, panic attacks and depression.

As a young doctor, Buteyko spent many months sitting at sick patients' bedsides observing their states of health. He noticed that each person's breathing got heavier as his or her health deteriorated. As their illnesses advanced, he saw that his patients breathing movements from their chests and tummies increased, that their breathing became more audible, that their breaths became faster and that they sighed more and breathed through their mouths. In time, he was able to predict the onset of death just by observing their breathing.

This raised a fundamental question for Buteyko: was it his patients' sickness that contributed to their heavy breathing or was it their heavy breathing that contributed to their sickness?

At the time, Buteyko suffered from severe hypertension that was going from bad to worse. He began experimenting by breathing less and quieting his breathing. Within a short while, the pains that he had experienced for months went away.

Over the following decades, Buteyko extensively researched this subject and had a dedicated laboratory to further his findings. His method was brought to the West in 1990 and is now taught in many countries.

Breathing, such a vital factor for life, must meet certain conditions. Severe overbreathing can be fatal if sustained over a short period. Therefore, it is plausible to accept that negative health effects will result from less severe but still excessive breathing over a long period.

OVERBREATHING

Chronic overbreathing basically means that we habitually breathe more air than what our bodies require. In many ways, this is similar to a person developing the habit of overeating.

Breathing is similar. If we breathe more than what our bodies require over a 24-hour period, the habit takes hold. Dr Stephen Demeter confirms this when he states, "Prolonged hyperventilation (for more than 24 hours) seems to sensitize the brain, leading to a more prolonged hyperventilation."[1]

What increases breathing volume?

Breathing increases as a result of modern living. Factors such as strong emotions, tension, anger, stress, overeating, processed foods, a belief that taking big breaths is good, lack of exercise, excessive talking and high temperatures within the home all contribute to overbreathing.

HOW TO RECOGNISE
HABITUAL OVERBREATHING

At this point, you might think that your child does not overbreathe. For most children, overbreathing is subtle. It is hidden, which is why it often goes undetected. The typical breathing habits of children, teenagers and adults attending my clinics include:

- Breathing through the mouth;
- Audible breathing during rest;
- Regular sighs;
- Regular sniffing;
- Irregular breathing;
- Holding of the breath (apnoea);
- Taking large breaths prior to talking;
- Yawning with big breaths;
- Upper chest movement;
- Movement of shoulders while breathing;
- Lot of visible movement;
- Effortful breathing;
- Heavy breathing at night.

How many apply to your child? Does your child sigh? Does your child breathe through their mouth? Do they wake up with a dry mouth in the morning?

HOW SHOULD WE BREATHE?

CARBON DIOXIDE

Both oxygen and carbon dioxide play a fundamental role during breathing. While there is an abundant supply of oxygen in the form of fresh air, carbon dioxide must be produced and stored by the body. Contrary to popular belief, not all oxygen is good and not all carbon dioxide is bad. For example; too much oxygen generates free radicals which attack other cells causing disease and aging, while too little carbon dioxide affects how the body utilises oxygen. For normal healthy functioning, it is vital that both gases meet a certain level.

During normal conditions, 75% of our intake of oxygen is exhaled while breathing a healthy volume of four to six litres per minute. Even during intense exercise, it is estimated that 25% of our oxygen intake is exhaled. Breathing a volume of air greater than normal does not increase the amount of oxygen in our blood, as it is already 97-98% saturated. In other words, there are no benefits to breathing more air than what the body requires.

Carbon dioxide or CO_2 is a gas created as an end product from our metabolic process. The human lungs require 5% CO_2 or 40 mmHg. If we breathe too much, CO_2 is exhaled or washed from our lungs. A loss of CO_2 from the lungs results in a reduction of CO_2 in the blood, tissues and cells.

The release of oxygen from red blood cells depends on the partial pressure or quantity of carbon dioxide in your lungs/arterial blood. When one is overbreathing, carbon dioxide is removed from the body, causing the oxygen to "stick" to haemoglobin within the red blood cells. This prevents its release into tissues and organs. This bond, discovered in 1904, is known as the Bohr Effect.

THE BOHR EFFECT SIMPLY EXPLAINED

Healthy children and teenagers have quiet and unnoticeable breathing. While they are resting, you cannot see or hear their breathing. Quiet breathing ensures optimum partial pressure of carbon dioxide within their lungs, blood, tissues and cells. The release of oxygen from the blood depends on the presence of carbon dioxide. Overbreathing causes a loss of carbon dioxide from the lungs, blood, tissues and cells. This results in less oxygen being released from the blood into the tissues and organs. The more your child breathes, the more their body is being starved of oxygen. Breathing through the mouth, sighs, sniffing, noticeable breathing, hearing breathing during rest or having low steps or Control Pause (explained later) indicates that your child is starving their body of oxygen. The calmer and quieter your child breathes, the more their blood vessels open, enabling better circulation and distribution of oxygen throughout the body, including the brain. To oxygenate your brain-breathe correctly.

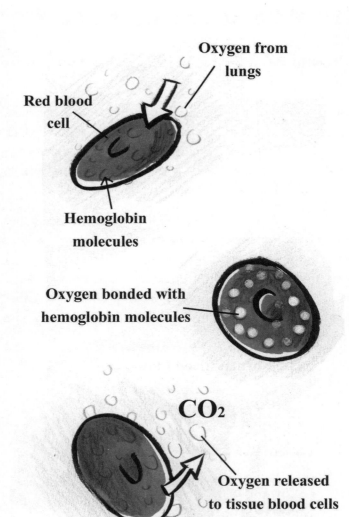

Oxygen from lungs

Red blood cell

Hemoglobin molecules

Oxygen bonded with hemoglobin molecules

CO_2

Oxygen released to tissue blood cells

IMPROVE OXYGENATION

Carbon dioxide relaxes the smooth muscles that surround the airways, arteries and capillaries.

With a normal breathing volume of 5 litres of air per minute, the partial pressure of carbon dioxide amounts to 40mmHg. Each 1 mmHg drop of arterial CO_2 reduces blood flow to the brain by 2%.[2] In other words, oxygenation of your child's brain significantly decreases when they breathe heavily.

The heavier your child breathes, the more they feed their hyperventilation or overbreathing related problems. Is your child tired in the morning after a night's breathing through the mouth? Do they snore? Do they hold their breath during sleep? Are their tonsils enlarged? Do they wet the bed? How is their concentration? Are they anxious? Do they have a blocked nose, cough or wheeze?

Normal Blood Flow

Restricted Blood Flow

SYMPTOMS OF CHRONIC HYPERVENTILATION

- **Neurological:** light-headed feeling, poor concentration, memory lapses, faintness, headache, anxiety, tension, racing mind, numbness and tingling, tremor, depression, apprehension, irritability, brain fog, panic attacks, disrupted sleep, detachment from reality and stress.
- **Heart:** palpitations, a racing heartbeat, pain in the chest region and a skipping or irregular heartbeat.
- **Respiratory system:** wheezing, breathlessness, coughing, frequent colds and chest infections, chest tightness, frequent yawning, snoring and sleep apnoea.
- **Gastrointestinal:** Esophagal reflux, heartburn, aerophagia.

Other general symptoms include eczema, psoriasis, mouth dryness, fatigue, bad dreams, sleep disturbance, nightmares, ADHD, dry itchy skin, sweating, cramping, spasm, increased urination such as bed wetting or regular visits to the bathroom during the night, diarrhoea, constipation, general weakness and chronic exhaustion.

HOW MIGHT IT APPLY TO YOUR CHILD?

Dr Kathleen Mary Fay is a board certified paediatrician. Based on her experience with her own child who suffered sleep and behavioural issues, she wrote a book entitled When crying it out does not work.[3]

She describes how only once during her 17 years of paediatric practise did she observe textbook recommendations working the way they claimed they would. In that case, the mother left her 11 month old in a crib to cry it out and did not return until the morning. This continued for several nights until the child slept quietly. As a parent of a young infant, I could only imagine the stress that both parent and child went through to achieve this.

Dr Fay also tried crying it out with her own son, but it was entirely unsuccessful. When he did sleep, he would awake shortly afterwards and the cycle would begin again.

"Then a miracle happened.....His main problem was his little runny nose." She brought him to a specialist who cleared the runny nose resulting in "a remarkable change in how he acted." Her child was less hyperactive, calmer with better concentration.[3]

Her son exhibited the typical consequences of any child who has habitual mouth breathing — he looked pale, was tired and had dark circles under his eyes.

Naturally, a child will mouth breathe when their nose gets blocked. This mouth breathing habit "wreaked havoc" on her son's sleep.

Her son's "miracle" compelled her to trawl through the medical literature to understand the change to her child after he was able to breathe through his nose.

She goes on to say; "Reading the adult medical literature, I learned that older patients with allergic rhinitis complained about daytime tiredness and that this improved with treatment of their nasal congestion. There was also a wealth of information about breathing difficulties causing insomnia in adults, and that this insomnia could be worsened by anxiety. As I read, I realized that sleepless children who fought bedtime or woke parents at night might not have behaviour problems caused by the parents. These children might be suffering from insomnia, and when I realized this, things started to fall into place for me. My son's initial sleep problems had been misdiagnosed as a "behavioural," so he had never been properly treated, and because he continued to have trouble sleeping, he also developed daytime problems with behaviour and school work, which were the result of his being overtired."[3]

Dr Fay's experience is borne out by a paper published in the January 2010 edition of General Dentistry. Author of the paper, Dr Yosh Jefferson says:

"Children who mouth breathe typically do not sleep well, causing them to be tired during the day and possibly unable to concentrate on academics." He goes onto say that "if the child becomes frustrated in school, he or she may exhibit behavioural problems."[4]

"Many of these children are misdiagnosed with attention deficit disorder and hyperactivity (ADD/ADHD). In addition, mouth breathing can cause poor oxygen concentration in the blood stream which can cause high blood pressure, heart problems, sleep apnoea and other medical conditions."[4]

GROWING THE PERFECT FACE

WHO IS DR MEW?

Dr John Mew is an orthodontist living and working in London. He graduated in dentistry from University College London, and then trained in Orthognathic surgery at the Royal Victoria Hospital, East Grinstead where he developed an interest in the science of facial growth. In 1965, he returned to University College to specialise in orthodontics. Since then, he has been developing non-surgical methods of correcting unattractive vertical growth in children's faces.

Dr Mew's family has an excellent tradition of dentistry, as his father was a dentist and his son, Dr Mike Mew, is an orthodontist.

A good-looking face is determined by a strong, sturdy chin, developed jaws, high cheekbones, good lips, correct nose size and straight teeth. When a face develops correctly, it follows that the teeth will be straight. Straight teeth do not create a good-looking face, but a good-looking face will create straight teeth.

Each year, parents spend thousands of pounds and dollars in an effort to straighten their child's teeth, while ignoring other factors. Dr Mew's work is to ensure the normal development of a child's face and teeth by correcting habits and by applying non-invasive techniques.

DR MEW'S PATIENTS

Over the past few decades, Dr Mew's assistant has taken a photograph of the face of every child that Dr Mew has treated. This ten-year-old boy is a nose breather and has a good-looking, broad face with everything in proportion. In other words, everything is in its right place. The boy exhibits well-defined eyes, cheekbones, lips and chin.

On the boy's fourteenth birthday, he was given a gerbil as a present. Soon after, his nose began to block, causing him to breathe through his mouth. Within three years, his face had changed its shape considerably.

The following photographs are of the boy at age seventeen. Because he kept his mouth open from the ages of 14 until 17, his face grew downwards instead of in width. His face

Courtesy Dr John Mew

became narrow and long. His jaws are set back from their perfect and natural position. He now has a double chin and his jaws come back on his airways, resulting in smaller airways. This creates health

Courtesy Dr John Mew

problems such as sleep apnoea. His nose looks far bigger because his jaws do not come forward enough, and his cheeks are sunken as his face drags everything downwards. This face is typical of the thousands of children who breathe through their mouths.

In many ways, the boy's face reminds me of my own face. I was a mouth breather until the age of 25, and know too well the health consequences. Making a change to nasal breathing changed my life in every way. The benefits that I experienced included better sleep, no more snoring, more energy, better concentration, no more asthma attacks, no need for asthma medication, and a far calmer disposition. In addition, I am now embarking on orthotropic treatment to expand my jaws to make room for my existing teeth, something that my tongue would have done had I been encouraged to breathe through my nose as a child.

TWO SISTERS

Kelly (left) was seven years old and Samantha (right) was eight-and-a-half years old. Both sisters displayed habitual mouth breathing and were developing associated facial growth patterns. They attended Dr Mew, who taught them to breathe through their noses and to swallow correctly.

Kelly   Samantha

Courtesy Dr John Mew

Kelly took on all that Dr Mew told her, but her older sister Samantha was more complacent. She did not keep her mouth closed while breathing.

Both girls returned a few years later. Again, Dr Mew's assistant took follow-up photographs, which are shown below. Kelly is to the left and Samantha is to the right.

Kelly   Samantha

Courtesy Dr John Mew

Observe the development of their faces. In your view, who has the more attractively defined face? Look at the tension on Samantha's mouth as she closes her mouth for the photograph.

EVOLUTION OF CROOKED TEETH

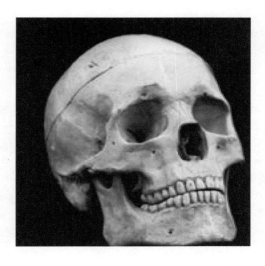

The human lineage can be traced without break from Homo erectus who existed on Earth approximately 600,000 years ago. Throughout this time, humans have exhibited straight teeth. If one visits a natural history museum and examine the skulls of prehistoric man, wide facial structures and straight teeth would be evident. Crooked teeth are a modern day phenomena. Even as late as the 1600s, crooked teeth – while present amongst the wealthier class – affected only a small portion of the population. "Research has shown that this degeneration has become more marked within the past 400 years, and in European countries again appears to be linked with social progress and possibly a change of diet."[1]

DIET AND MOUTH BREATHING

Over seventy years ago, dentist Dr Weston Price visited many primitive and isolated groups such as aborigines, Gaelic people, Swiss people, Eskimos, North American Indians and Maoris. His interest was in determining the effect of a change from their traditional to a more modernised European diet. His findings are published in a highly informative book entitled Nutrition and Physical Degeneration.[2]

Dr Price noted that when the Gaelic people, living on the Hebrides off the coast of Scotland, changed from their traditional diet of small seafoods and oatmeal to a modernised diet of "angel food cake, white bread and many white flour commodities, marmalade, canned vegetables, sweetened fruit juices, jams, and confections," first-generation children became mouth breathers and their immunity from the diseases of civilisation reduced dramatically.[2]

One of his observations is as follows: "The change in the two generations was illustrated by a little girl and her grandfather on the Isle of Skye. He was the product of the old regime, and about eighty years of age. He was typical of the stalwart product raised on the native foods.

His granddaughter had pinched nostrils and narrowed face. Her dental arches were deformed and her teeth crowded. She was a mouth breather. She had the typical expression of the result of modernisation after the parents had adopted the modern foods of commerce, and abandoned the oatcake, oatmeal porridge and sea foods."[2]

Recognizing the fact that children become mouth breathers is significant and illustrates the link between the modern diet and chronic mouth breathing. As a child experiences a greater demand to breathe heavier, he or she opens his or her mouth to breathe, thus causing craniofacial changes and negatively impacting his or her health. Increased breathing volume in turn affects immunity responses, often resulting in a blocked nose and thus completing the cycle.

THE BIG TEETHED MULE

Of all the species on earth, humans are most affected by crooked teeth. The traditional explanation is that the child inherited smaller jaws from his or her mother and larger teeth from his or her father. Could this be true?

In the aptly entitled book, Why Raise Ugly Kids? Dr Hal A. Huggins questions the genetic argument and cites his observation of working on the family farm. One comment is as follows: "Horse and donkey – cross them and you get a fine work animal. Used them a lot on the farm and know what? I never saw a mule with horse's teeth and a donkeys jaw."[3]

Dogs, with the exception of those who have been crossbred, are another good example, as the pups of a labrador father and poodle mother will have straight teeth. "Domestic dogs don't develop malocclusions (crooked teeth) unless they are selectively crossbred for the purpose as with bulldogs."[1]

According to Australian orthodontist Dr John Flutter, "every child's face has the growth potential to match its own set of teeth."[5] Bearing this in mind, Dr Mike Mew advocates that "there is no evidence that we should not accommodate 32 well aligned teeth today or that there has been any genetic change."[4]

MOUTH BREATHING CAUSES CROOKED TEETH

During the 1960s, dentist Egil P Harvold recognised that "oral respiration associated with obstruction of the nasal airway is a common finding among patients seeking orthodontic treatment."[6] To determine the relationship between mouth breathing and crooked teeth, he conducted a number of experiments by blocking the noses of young monkeys with silicon nose plugs.

"The experiments showed that the monkeys adapted to nasal obstruction in different ways. In general, the experimental animals maintained an open mouth. All experimental animals gradually acquired a facial appearance and dental occlusion different from those of the control animals."[6] The mouth-breathing monkeys developed crooked teeth and other facial deformities, including "a lowering of the chin, a steeper mandibular plane angle, and an increase in the gonial angle as compared with the eight control animals."[7]

Harvold claimed to be able to reproduce the equivalent of most human dental irregularities; "Any common type of dental irregularity can be produced experimentally in monkeys with normal dentition."[1] In support of Harvold's findings, Dr Mew states that "it is hard to escape the conclusion that in monkeys, a change in the action and posture of the tongue can produce severe malocclusions."[1]

EVERY CHILD HAS THE POTENTIAL TO GROW AN ATTRACTIVE FACE

Toddlers and young children generally have well defined, broad and good-looking faces. However, a different story emerges with many teenagers. A visit to a high school will uncover many long, narrow and flat faces with sunken cheek bones, receded chins, narrow jaws and prominent noses. So what happens in the interim? Why do children develop crooked teeth and narrow faces?

Page age 5y 6m   **Age 7y 10m**

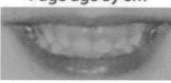 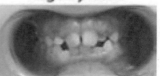

Courtesy Dr John Mew

Many young children have beautifully straight teeth at the age of five or six but the teeth and face can quickly change if they leave their mouth open (see previous page).

Consensus from thousands of orofacial myologists, hygienists, dentists, orthodontists and published papers worldwide is that for the face and, consequently, teeth to develop correctly, a number of factors must be employed by the growing child. Such factors include:

1. Mouth closed with lips gently together;
2. Three quarters of the tongue resting in the roof of the mouth, with the tip of the tongue placed before the front teeth;
3. Breathing through the nose;
4. Correct swallowing;

According to Meredith, 60% of the growth of the face takes place during the first four years of life and 90% takes place by the age of 12. Development of the lower jaw continues until around age 18.[8]

Based on these observations, for correct craniofacial growth to take place, early intervention with nasal breathing and tongue posture is essential. In the words of Dr Carl Schreiner, "The deleterious effects of nasal obstruction are virtually complete by puberty so the window of opportunity is relatively brief. Delay in intervention may result in unsuccessful orthodontic treatment which may require orhthagnathic surgery at an older age."[9]

HOW CHILDREN DEVELOP CROOKED TEETH

The normal growth direction of the jaws is forward. This occurs as a result of the forces exerted by the lips and tongue. It works based on this same principal used by orthodontics: light forces move teeth.

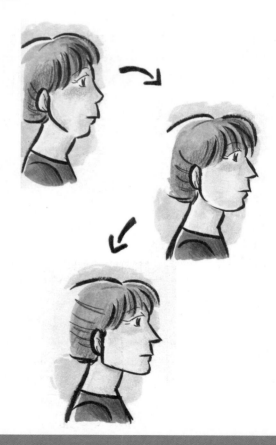

The lips exert an estimated pressure against the teeth of between 100 gm and 300 gm.[10] While swallowing, the pressure exerted against the anterior teeth by the tongue is estimated to be 500 gms,[11] while the force required to move a tooth is as small as 1.7gm.[5]

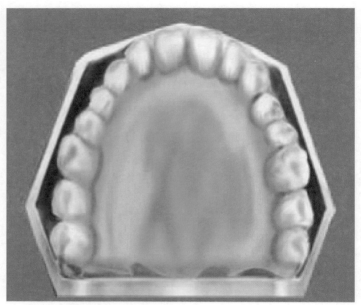

U-shaped top jaw

We swallow an estimated 2,000 times per day, and each time
we swallow, the tongue pushes upwards and flattens in the roof
of the mouth, exerting a considerable force that shapes the jaws.[5]
The correct position of the tongue is resting in the roof of the
mouth. As the child grows, the top jaw forms around the tongue.
In other words, the shape of the top jaw is the shape of the
tongue. As the tongue is U-shaped, it results in a broad facial
structure with sufficient room to house all teeth. Nature dictates
that the shape of the lower jaw will follow that of the top jaw.[5]

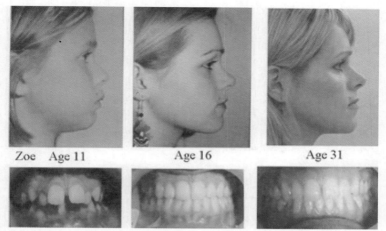

Zoe, illustrating forward growth of the face following treatment from Dr Mew. Courtesy of Dr John Mew

When the mouth is open, the tongue cannot rest in the roof of the mouth, resulting in a poorer developed, narrow, V-shaped top jaw. A smaller top jaw leads to a narrow facial structure and overcrowding of the teeth. "Low tongue posture seen with oral respiration (mouth breathing) impedes the lateral expansion and anterior development of the maxilla (top jaw)."[12]

In the words of dentist Dr Raymond Silkman, "The most important orthodontic appliance that you all have and carry with you twenty-four hours a day is your tongue. People who breathe through their nose normally have a tongue that postures up into the maxilla (the top jaw). When the tongue sits right up behind the front teeth, it is maintaining the shape of the maxilla (top jaw) every time you swallow. Every time the proper tongue swallow motion takes place, it spreads up against the maxilla (top jaw), activating it and contributing to that little cranial motion. Individuals who breathe through their mouths have a lower tongue posture and the maxilla does not receive the stimulation from the tongue that it should."[13]

This is supported by Dr John Flutter's statement: "There is no doubt that the tongue has an enormous influence on dentition,"[14] and by Dr Mew's statement:

"Lack of tongue pressure hinders the growth of the maxilla (top jaw). Put conversely, the maxilla may not be able to achieve its inherited potential without assistance from tongue posture."[1]

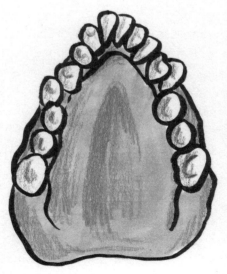

V-shaped top jaw

During an interview on the Australian TV programme "Sixty Seconds," Australian orthodontist Dr Derek Mahony talks of one of his patients: "If you look at Zoe, what's caused all this crowding is really not genetics, it's more related to the way she breathes and, if you open really wide there, Zoe, you can see that narrow, top jaw V-shape arch."[16]

He goes on to say, "the key to diagnosing the problem is starting treatment at an early age. And the problem often starts here in the roof of the mouth. When children suck their thumbs or breathe through their mouths, it can be pushed in and this narrowing can have a knock-on effect. The lower jaw is forced back and down, producing what most of us would call buck teeth."

CRANIOFACIAL ABNORMALITIES

It is well documented that mouth-breathing children grow longer faces. A paper by Tourne entitled *The long face syndrome and impairment of the nasopharyngeal airway*, recognised that "the switch from a nasal to an oronasal (mouth and nose combined) breathing pattern induces functional adaptations that include an increase in total anterior face height and vertical development of the lower anterior face."[17]

In another paper, Dr Carl Schreiner comments that "Long-standing nasal obstruction appears to affect craniofacial morphology during periods of rapid facial growth in genetically susceptible children with narrow facial pattern."[18]

In a paper entitled, *Care of nasal airway to prevent orthodontic problems in children,* "a mouth breather lowers the tongue position to facilitate the flow of air in to the expanding lungs. The resultant effect is maldevelopment of the jaw in particular and deformity of the face in general. Setting of the teeth on the jaw is also affected. All these make the face look negative. So, to prevent orthodontic problems in children, it is necessary to detect the nasopharyngeal obstruction and treat the same accordingly." [19]

In a study of 47 children between the ages of 6 to 15 years that was done to determine the correlation between breathing mode and craniofacial morphology, "findings demonstrated a significant predominance of mouth breathing compared to nasal breathing in the vertical growth patterns studied." The paper concluded that, "results show a correlation between obstructed nasal breathing, large adenoids and vertical growth pattern." [20]

Another study involving 73 children between the ages of 3 to 6 years that was done to determine the influence of mouth breathing on dentofacial growth and development concluded that "mouth breathing can influence craniofacial and occlusal development early in childhood." [21]

In a paper entitled "*Malocclusion and upper airway obstruction,*" [49] children with confirmed nasal obstruction were studied. The paper noted that "the main characteristics of the respiratory obstruction syndrome (blocked nose) are presence of hypertrophied tonsils or adenoids, mouth breathing, open bite, cross bite, excessive anterior face height, incompetent lip posture, excessive appearance of maxillary anterior teeth, narrow external nares, V-shaped maxillary arch (top jaw)." [15]

When the tongue is not resting in the roof of the mouth, the jaws are impeded from growing forward and are instead set back from their ideal position. This contracts the airways, contributing to breathing difficulties and sleep apnoea. In addition, the nose will seem larger, similar to that of a roman nose. The "nose is more pronounced in an ideal occlusion (straight teeth) but in the various malocclusions (crooked teeth) where the maxilla (top jaw) is underdeveloped it appears larger, although in fact it is smaller."[1]

"Lack of growth affects the whole face and is associated with flat cheeks, unattractive lips, large noses, tired eyes, double chin, receding chins and sloping forehead, features that will be readily recognised when there is a pronounced crowding of teeth."[22]

Given the extent of information available, it is surprising that few dentists seem to be aware of the craniofacial effects from mouth breathing. The journal General Dentist noted that "the vast majority of health care professionals are unaware of the negative impact of upper airway obstruction (mouth breathing) on normal facial growth and physiologic health. Children whose mouth breathing is untreated may develop long, narrow faces, narrow mouths, high palatal vaults, dental malocclusion (crooked teeth), gummy smiles and many other unattractive facial features. These children do not sleep well at night due to obstructed airways; this lack of sleep can adversely affect their growth and academic performance. Many of these children are misdiagnosed with attention deficit disorder (ADD) and hyperactivity." The paper further states that "if mouth breathing is treated early, its negative effect on facial and dental development and the medical and social problems associated with it can be reduced or averted."[23]

REVERSIBLE AT AN EARLY AGE

Learning correct breathing and swallowing before the age of eight years often corrects facial development without the need for any orthodontic treatment. As the lower jaws are still developing until the age of eighteen, teenagers can also derive considerable benefit.

Furthermore, the success of any orthodontic treatment depends on the application of correct breathing and swallowing. Estimates in the field are that up to 90% of orthodontic work relapses unless poor oral habits such as mouth breathing are addressed.[5]

In a paper entitled, *Nasal obstruction in children and secondary dental deformities*, "Effective orthodontic therapy may require the elimination of the nasal obstruction to allow for normalization of the facial musculature surrounding the dentition."[9] In other words, for orthodontic treatment to be effective, patients must be taught how to unblock their noses, breathe through their noses and swallow correctly.

During the 70s and 80s, Linder-Aronsen consistently noted the relationship between nasal obstruction and craniofacial changes, including longer faces, open bite and cross bite. More importantly, significant craniofacial changes toward normal were observed to take place after patients returned to nasal breathing.[24,25,26,27]

In another study of 26 children, Kerr showed how development of the lower jaws began to normalise after they switched from mouth to nasal breathing.[28]

Finally, "Evidence of reversibility" is also strongly supported by studies of monozygotic twins in which one developed nasal obstruction due to trauma. The obstructed twin developed characteristics of the long face syndrome which partially normalized following correction of the (nasal) obstruction."[9]

ORTHODONTICS: CHOOSE WISELY!

For parents embarking upon orthodontic treatment to advance the health and facial appearance of their children, there is much concern among the world's scientific community over the lack of science in current clinical practise.[29,30,31,32]

Conventional orthodontic treatment is unable to replicate the straight teeth that develop naturally when the mouth is closed and the tongue is resting in the roof of the mouth. According to orthodontist Dr John Flutter, "the best aligned teeth I see are people who never had orthodontic treatment."[5]

Traditional orthodontics recognises the cause of crooked teeth as a result of teeth being too large for the jaws. The approach is to wait until the child is twelve years of age or older before treatment begins. Normally, two to four teeth are extracted to make room for existing teeth, which are then aligned with braces.

UK-based Channel Four programme called Dispatches that aired during December 1999, queried whether the standard orthodontic treatment of extractions to make room for teeth actually damages a child's face.[33,34] The programme showed that parents who bring their children with crooked teeth to an orthodontist are not told that the treatment could cause serious damage.

During the programme, 700 UK families were interviewed. More than half of the children undergoing treatment had teeth extracted. A comparison was made with treatment in California, where extractions take place in only 15% of cases.[33,34] There, many orthodontists apply expandable braces to gently widen the jaws to make room for the teeth. In addition, children are taught exercises, including correct swallowing and nasal breathing, as part of their treatment.

In an interview with the British newspaper, The Independent, Dr Mew is quoted as follows: "I frequently see examples of faces which have been really badly spoiled. In my personal opinion, probably about 20 per cent of orthodontic patients are noticeably damaged and maybe another 30 per cent are slightly damaged."[34]

The article further adds that extraction of teeth can result in "long-term damage to the skull, jaw pain and headaches as a result of orthodontic dentistry. In the worst cases, they suffer ringing in the ears, postural problems leading to muscle pain in the neck, shoulders and back, and extreme headaches."[3]

The best advice if you are considering orthodontic treatment for your child is to ask your orthodontist whether there will be room for all 32 teeth and also check that the vertical growth of the child's face will not be increased. If you don't receive such an assurance, you might be wise to ask for a second opinion.

IDENTICAL TWINS

Identical Twins to compare results

Age 8   **FIXED WITH PREMOLAR EXTS**   Age 13

He is now in fixed retainers

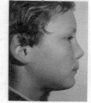   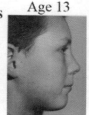

ORTHOTROPIC TREATMENT

No fixed appliances, no extractions, no
retention and no relapse

   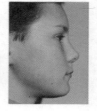

Courtesy of Dr John Mew. (Ben pictured above. Quinton pictured below)

One case that Dr Mew puts forward to support his claims is the case history of identical twin brothers Quinton and Ben Creed who are pictured above. Quinton, the more serious case, was treated by Dr Mew using orthotropics which involved no extractions or braces. He reshaped Quinton's jaw with appliances to make room for the overcrowded teeth. His twin brother Ben opted for traditional orthodontics, resulting in the extraction of four teeth and fixed braces.

A number of years later, Ben is quoted as saying "Because of the extractions, the width of my mouth is smaller. In hindsight, I would have preferred to have gone with Dr Mew's method as it got much better results."[34]

"I've got a longer face, a smaller smile, less pronounced features and just generally more of a flatter face." When Ben was asked if this was the result of his braces and extractions, he replied; "yes, it's probably due to the extractions and the braces that I had."[16]

Ever since the 1960s, Dr Mew's treatment is based on "aiming to encourage horizontal growth of the facial bones by means of good muscle tone and a tongue-to-palate resting posture with the mouth closed, in the belief that, in these circumstances, the teeth will align themselves. This is in contrast to the mechanical approach of most orthodontists, which innumerable papers have shown tends to increase vertical growth."[35]

In a paper by Dr Mew published in the *World Journal of Orthodontics*, a study compared the effect of traditional fixed appliances and orthotropic (growth guidance) treatment without fixed appliances on a series of identical twins ten years after treatment. A panel of 12 lay judges assessed the facial changes. "The results showed that most of the traditionally treated twins were judged to look less attractive after treatment, while most treated by Orthotropics were judged to have improved. There was little difference in the dental results, but the traditionally treated cases seemed to relapse more frequently."[36]

SIXTY MINUTES TV INTERVIEW

Australian TV programme Sixty Minutes interviewed a number of orthodontists on this subject. The interviewer was Peter Overton. Dr Geoff Wexler was spokesman for the Australian Society of Orthodontists. The following is part of the transcript.[16]

PETER OVERTON: Well, how about this example. Nineteen-year-old Michael Buggy went to six Sydney orthodontists for his condition, some minor crowding. All insisted he lose four teeth. But his mother Valerie wasn't so sure.

VALERIE BUGGY: And I was horrified, because I didn't think that he had such a big problem and I begged them not to take them out. I said, "Isn't there, in all the knowledge that you have and all the studying that you've done, isn't there another way?" But they were quite steadfast that no, the teeth have got to come out or the problem would come back.

PETER OVERTON: Finally Valerie gave in and took Michael to the dentist for the extractions.

VALERIE BUGGY: He was just at the point of having them out, she had all the tools in her hand and she said, "You don't want this to happen, do you?" And I said, "No, I don't, but what else can I do?" And as luck would have it she gave me this dentist's card and said, "Give him a ring."

PETER OVERTON: That card belonged to Derek Mahony and he straightened Michael's teeth without extractions.

VALERIE BUGGY: I would like to actually show these orthodontists that said to me, "You'll be back, you'll be sorry." I'd like to show them his smile now and I just wish that orthodontists would get together and give any mother like me the opportunity not to have the teeth taken out.

PETER OVERTON: Can I show you this patient here? Do you think he needs extractions?

DR GEOFF WEXLER: Well, I wouldn't.

PETER OVERTON: You wouldn't?

DR GEOFF WEXLER: No.

PETER OVERTON: Six eminent orthodontists recommended to this patient's mother that he needed to have the classic four on the floor.

DR GEOFF WEXLER: What you've presented me here is part of the information. Based on what you've shown me I wouldn't, but there might be other factors that you haven't shown me in this patient's diagnosis.

PETER OVERTON: He's had very successful treatment with Derek Mahony without extractions. Does that surprise you?

DR GEOFF WEXLER: No.

PETER OVERTON: Are faces being damaged by traditional extraction-type orthodontics?

DR GEOFF WEXLER: I haven't seen any evidence at all to say that faces are being damaged in general.

PETER OVERTON: Try telling that to dentist Dr Mike Fennel. He pulled out four of his son's teeth on the advice of an orthodontist. The result? David's face ended up looking like this.

DR MIKE FENNEL: It ruined the look of his mouth. So from the nose upwards he looked great, but from the nose downwards he just looked terrible, but how do you tell that to your son? In fact, he looked like an old man. At the age of 18 he looked like an old man with no teeth in.

PETER OVERTON: Is "damaged" the right word?

DR MIKE FENNEL: Yes, it is really.

PETER OVERTON: Traditional orthodontics did that to his face?

DR MIKE FENNEL: They did, yes. Yes.

Insanity: doing the same thing over and over again and expecting different results.

— Albert Einstein

EVERYTHING TO
CORRECT BREATHING

NOTE OF CAUTION

While breathing exercises are perfectly safe for most, they are not recommended for a number of children. If you are unsure, do not attempt breathing exercises. Instead contact me via contact information in the appendix.

Do not attempt any of the breathing exercises if your child has or is undergoing any of the following:

- Cancer treatment
- Type 1 diabetes
- Epilepsy
- Any heart problems in the past six months
- Kidney or brain conditions

Cleansing reactions

Some children who learn reduced breathing techniques experience a detox or cleansing reaction. This detox is due to improved blood flow and the oxygenation of all tissues and organs.

Note: if your child experiences an increased feeling of coldness as they apply reduced breathing, cease the exercise and consult with an experienced practitioner. An increased sensation of coldness can indicate a drop in blood sugar levels and a snack is recommended.

Generally, cleansing reactions are an aggravation of their usual symptoms, are mild and can last just one to two days.

Depending on the child, typical symptoms include:

- Diarrhoea
- Mucus from the nose or lungs
- More frequent visits to the bathroom
- Increased yawning and fatigue
- Insomnia
- General feeling of unwellness
- Short-term headache
- Increased demand for water.

To help reduce the intensity and duration of cleansing reactions, have your child drink warm water regularly throughout the day and continue with the exercise "many small breath holds" which is explained below.

On a positive note, your child will experience improvements in their health, including: increased calmness and concentration; less anxiety, stress and uncontrolled thought activity; better moods; better sleep; more energy; far less asthma and improved well being.

UNBLOCK THE NOSE

Free video excerpts www.ButeykoKids.com

Overbreathing causes a child's nose to become blocked. Many parents will question this conclusion, seeing allergies as the real cause. Surely the nose gets blocked due to pollen, dust mites, dairy, animal dander and other associated allergies?

Yes, the nose does block when some children and teenagers are exposed to these particles or foods but they are triggers only. The cause of the nasal obstruction is overbreathing.

To unblock the nose one needs to do the opposite to heavy breathing. In other words; hold the breath. This exercise will unblock the noses of all children and teenagers. Try it on yourself.

If your child is quite young or a beginner to this exercise, it can be very helpful to place paper tape over their mouth especially during the first few times of practise. A recommended tape is 3M micropore paper tape which can be purchased at most chemists.

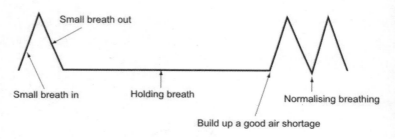

To explain each exercise, we use an imaginary little boy called Ryan.

- Ryan takes a gentle breath in through his nose (if nose is totally blocked, take tiny breath through corner of mouth)
- Ryan gently breathes out through his nose
- He then pinches his nose with his fingers to hold his breath
- He keeps his hand above his mouth so that mouth is visible
- Ryan sways his body or gently nods his head up and down to distract himself (Your child could also walk around while holding the breath)

- He pretends that he is underwater and he holds his breath for as long as possible
- When Ryan can hold his breath no more, he lets go of his nose and breathes through it
- He immediately calms his breathing
- He drops his shoulders and relaxes

Have your child wait for one minute and repeat. Continue to do this exercise until the nose gets free. Your child should practise any time the nose gets blocked.

When the child first breathes through their nose, their nostrils may flare and they might feel that they are not getting enough air. This is not because their nose is too small, it is because their breathing is too heavy. The respiratory centre within their brain has adjusted to a larger breathing volume and they are trying to take too much air in through their nose.

While the nose unblocking exercise will free the nose, it is not particularly effective at correcting breathing volume. The best exercises to correct breathing volume are "steps" and "reduced breathing." These exercises will eliminate the feeling that the child is not getting enough air when they breathe through their nose. Unless breathing volume is corrected, the child will find it very difficult to make a permanent switch to nasal breathing.

STEP IT UP!

The best exercise for children and teens are "steps". If the child is wheezing or coughing, steps should be avoided as it could disrupt their breathing. Instead practise "many small breath holds" (explained later) to stop the symptoms.

Steps involve walking as many steps as possible while holding the breath. The hold must be on the out breath. This exercise will help to correct breathing and ease the change from mouth to nasal breathing.

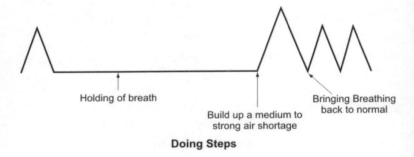

Holding of breath

Build up a medium to strong air shortage

Bringing Breathing back to normal

Doing Steps

To practise steps, Ryan does the following;

- He breathes out gently
- He pinches his nose with his fingers to hold the breath on the out breath
- He walks as many steps as possible
- When he feels a strong air shortage, he releases his fingers from his nose and breathes through his nose

- He calms his breathing in two breaths or so
- Someone counts aloud every ten steps to give feedback
- Ryan ensures that he does not be stressed

Typically children starting off will achieve about 20 steps. With regular practise of twelve repetitions each day, the child's steps should increase by about ten extra each week.

Important points

- Nose should be held with hand above the mouth leaving mouth visible to check if air is "sneaking in"
- If the child is unable to calm their breathing within two to three breaths, they have walked too many steps. The objective is for the child not to be stressed.
- Steps should be consistent. Older kids often reduce the size of each step in order to achieve more. Consistent steps will show a more realistic picture of their progress.
- The child can walk relatively fast or run if it is safe to do so.

Very young children should be encouraged to wear paper tape across their mouth while practising the steps. Otherwise, they will tend to allow air in through the mouth.

Another useful tip is for young children to walk between two points. Ask the child to walk from one person to another while holding the breath. If two adults are not available, have the child walk from a set point like a piece of furniture to the adult. When the child is comfortable with this, encourage them to double the distance. Over time gently increase the distance that the child walks. The child should be able to recover within two breaths.

Steps as a measurement;

If the steps are less than sixty; all symptoms such as mouth breathing, tiredness, poor sports fitness, blocked nose, coughing, wheezing, breathlessness, snoring, and disrupted sleep etc. are present.

If the steps are greater than sixty, main symptoms such as coughing, wheezing, blocked nose and tiredness will have disappeared but could be present if exposed to a trigger.

If the steps range from 80 to 100, it is highly unlikely for symptoms to be present. The goal is to achieve 100 steps plus.

REDUCED BREATHING

While the steps are the most important exercise for children and teens, it is essential to learn reduced breathing as it helps correct breathing volume and provides an understanding of good and bad breathing.

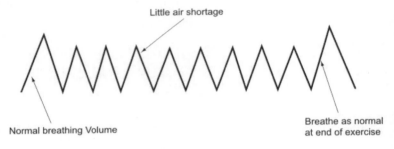

Little air shortage

Normal breathing Volume

Breathe as normal
at end of exercise

Creating a Little air shortage

Earlier on, we learned that good breathing is calm, quiet, silent and invisible. There are hardly any breathing movements from the tummy or chest.

Reduced breathing is breathing a volume of air which is less than what we usually breathe. The golden rule is that we are breathing less when we feel a medium shortage of air. A shortage of air is a want or need for air. It can also be described as a hunger for air. It is a feeling similar to the breathlessness experienced during a walk or run.

When a child or teenager correctly applies reduced breathing, you will see concentration on their face, their face will become red in colour and they feel warmer, their eyes become glassy and they may have more saliva in their mouths.

As a parent, keep an eye out for the glassy eyes and repeatedly ask the child how they feel. Do they want more air?

APPROACH ONE—
BLOCKING ONE NOSTRIL

Approach One is easy and involves Ryan stopping air flow to the clear nostril with his finger and breathing through the more blocked nostril. If Ryan can breathe easily through both nostrils, then he can practise approach two or three instead.

- Ryan sits up straight. (slouched posture sends breathing to the upper chest)
- He allows his shoulders to relax
- Ryan then finds which nostril is blocked by placing his finger over the left nostril and then over the right nostril
- He then places his finger over the free nostril so that he breathes through the partially blocked nostril
- Even if the nostril is quite blocked, Ryan continues to breathe through it. While Ryan might feel a strong need for air, the objective is that he does not feel stressed. (Often you will hear the child breathe while they block their free nostril. The most important thing is that they try to relax and quieten their breathing)

- Ryan continues to breathe through the blocked nostril for four minutes
- In a short time, Ryan's blocked nostril will free as he breathes through it

Now encourage your child to do the exercise. Did your child feel the air shortage?

APPROACH TWO—
HAND OVER FACE

- Ryan places his hand over his face
- He tries to feel the air flowing from his nose
- Ryan concentrates on the warm air as it leaves his nose and brushes against the palm of his hand
- He makes his breath shorter and smaller
- He pretends that there is a feather resting on the palm of his hand
- Ryan breathes quietly so that the feather does not blow away
- Ryan breathes a tiny amount of air in — just into the tips of his nostrils. He imagines just taking enough air to fill his nostrils and no more. A tiny breath in and a relaxed breath out.
- To reduce his breathing, Ryan makes the breath in smaller
- Ryan gently breathes out

As your child's breath in is small and the breath out is quiet and relaxed, he will feel a need or want for air. Try to continue this for four minutes. Unless your child feels a need for air, the exercise is not effective. Make sure that your child feels a need for air.

APPROACH THREE—RYAN HIDES HIS BREATHING

Ryan sits in front of a mirror and concentrates on the breathing movements of his chest and tummy. As he feels and follows each breath, he allows his breathing to quieten and relax. He encourages his breathing to calm down so that he can only see very small movements. He breathes so quietly in order to hide his breathing. He repeats to himself for his breathing to quieten, for his breathing to reduce, for his breathing to relax.

Ryan realises that the more he puffs and pants, the less oxygen is delivered to his tissues and organs. It seems contradictory, but to ensure maximum release of oxygen from blood vessels, breathing at rest must be quiet.

Ryan continues to hide his breathing for four minutes

- He allows his shoulders to relax
- His mouth is closed
- He allows his breathing to calm and become quiet
- Ryan brings relaxation to his chest and tummy from the inside
- As he relaxes, his breathing will become quiet
- Very little breathing movement can be seen
- No breathing can be heard
- Ryan feels a tolerable need for air
- He maintains this for about four to five minutes

Now, it's your child's turn. Did your child feel a need for air?

CORRECT TONGUE POSTURE

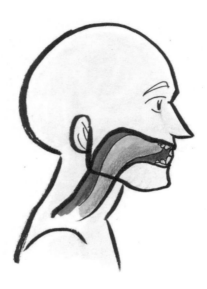

Did you know that humans are the only species who develop crooked teeth? With the exception of a very small number of dog breeds, all animals have straight teeth. Why would all animals have straight teeth and many humans have crooked teeth? What are we doing differently?

Did you also know that prehistoric man had straight teeth? For tens of thousands of years, our ancestors were fine specimens. They had broad faces with strong jaws and straight teeth. On the other hand, modern man has a narrow face with receded chin and crooked teeth!

What are the factors that ensure straight teeth?

1. The mouth must be closed at all times with lips together.
2. Three quarters of the tongue should be occupying the roof of the mouth with the tip resting gently behind but not against the top front teeth. The tongue shapes the top jaw by resting in the roof of the mouth.
3. Correct swallowing should involve the tongue moving upwards into the roof of mouth.

According to Dr Mew, tongue posture is more important than function. His *Tropic Premise* (1966) is quite specific; "The tongue should rest against the palate with the lips lightly sealed and the teeth in contact between 4 and 8 hours a day."

Where is your child's tongue when they breathe through their mouth?

To illustrate, Ryan does the following

- He opens his mouth
- Ryan says "N"
- He places three quarters of his tongue in the roof of the mouth with the tip resting on the "N" spot but not pushing against the teeth
- He now tries to breathe through his mouth with his tongue on the "N" spot

While this is possible to do, it is awkward and no child would breathe this way long term. The result is that habitual mouth breathers do not have their tongue resting in the roof of the mouth. Instead it rests midway or on the floor of the mouth. This has serious negative consequences on your child's facial growth.

CORRECT SWALLOW

The resting position of the tongue is in the roof of the mouth. When we swallow correctly, the tongue moves upwards and flattens out in the roof of the mouth. This action shapes the top jaw. The shape of the top jaw is the shape of the tongue. A well developed top jaw is optimal for housing all of our top teeth.

An incorrect swallow is when the tongue does not move up into the roof of the mouth. Instead the tongue pushes against the front or side teeth. This pushes the teeth forward or to the side. This is called a thrust and eventually a large gap may occur between the teeth.

Exercise to swallow correctly

Dr Mew teaches an exercise to help correct the swallow. The "N" spot is the place where you place your tongue in order to create the sound "N." Again, Ryan illustrates how to do this exercise.

- For this Ryan needs an ice cream wafer.
- He breaks off a piece about the size of a quarter, 10p or one euro coin.
- He chews until it can be made into a ball.
- Ryan makes a hollow with his tongue and positions the ball near the front.

- He places the tip of his tongue on the "N spot" but not pushing against the top front teeth.
- Ryan closes his teeth firmly together, pressing his tongue upwards and firmly against the skin in the roof of his mouth and swallows, sucking at the same time.
- Ryan keeps his lips apart in a big grin so that an adult can observe how he did.
- Ryan uses a mirror afterwards to see that no particles are left on his tongue.

Correct swallowing is very important to ensure correct development of the jaws. With a correct swallow, there is no movement from the outside of the face.

HOW TO STOP COUGH AND WHEEZE

Free video excerpts www.ButeykoKids.com

When youngsters breathe heavily either through the nose or mouth, their airways—depending on genetic predisposition—will narrow and become sensitive. This causes a cough, wheeze or chest tightness.

As a youngster, I had years of wheezing. Before the wheeze began, I would feel my breathing becoming a little more difficult. The natural response to my more difficult breathing was to breathe faster in an effort to take more air into my lungs. This in turn would feed my wheezing. The more air I took into my lungs, the more I would wheeze. I didn't know it at the time, but I was making my wheeze worse by breathing too much.

Any time you feel that your breathing is becoming more difficult, practise this exercise straight away to calm it down.

Many small breath holds

- Ryan gently breathes in through his nose
- He gently breathes out through his nose and pinches his nose with fingers

- He holds his breath for 3-5 seconds
- Ryan then releases his nose and breathes normally through it for ten seconds
- He repeats by holding his breath for 3 to 5 seconds
- He then breathes normally for ten seconds
- He continues with this exercise- hold breath for 3 to 5 seconds, breathe normally for ten seconds, holds breath for 3 to 5 seconds, breathe normally for ten seconds etc.

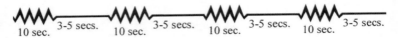

Points to bear in mind:

During wheezing and coughing, your child should not try to hold their breath for longer than 3 to 5 seconds because it would only increase their breathing, which may aggravate their symptoms. Nor should they practise the "Steps" exercise.

After each breath hold, your child breathes normally for about 10 seconds. Your child shouldn't interfere with their breathing.

Encourage your child to do a small breath hold followed by about 10 seconds normal breathing until their symptoms have passed.

VERY IMPORTANT: TAKE MEDICATION

Breathing exercises will only alleviate asthma when applied during the early stages of symptoms. If an asthma attack has been occurring for more than five minutes it will be a lot more difficult to control using breathing exercises. After 5 minutes of an attack your child should take their medication. (If they are having a severe attack—have them take their medication immediately). If they do not respond to medication within 5 minutes, seek medical attention immediately.

Many small breath holds used to stop coughing

With each cough, the child takes a large breath and this feeds into their next cough. The cycle has begun: another big breath, another cough, and more heavy breathing and so the merry-go-round continues.

This cycle can be broken by taking the following approach:

• When Ryan feels a cough coming, he tries to suppress his cough and not to cough at all. Sometimes, he will experience a ticklish feeling in his throat, but after a while his urge to cough should decline. Swallowing or holding his breath will help to curb the urge to cough.

- If Ryan still needs to cough, he tries to cough only through his nose. He tries to keep his cough quiet; to cough so quietly so that no one can hear him.
- Ryan understands that if a cough is forceful, it is loud and this will make his coughing worse.
- In between coughing, he uses many small breath holds exercise as described above until his coughing has stopped.

You might need to spend a lot of time encouraging your child to do many small breath holds. This exercise will greatly reduce and often stop the cough altogether eliminating the possibility of it developing into a severe attack.

LIFESTYLE

SNORING AND SLEEP APNOEA

Free video excerpts www.ButeykoKids.com

If your child is breathing through their mouth during sleep, they may experience many of the symptoms below.

How many do they experience?

- Snoring
- Sleep apnoea (holding the breath many times throughout the night)
- Disrupted sleep
- Restless sleep
- Sweating
- Nightmares
- Wetting the bed during the night
- Fatigue first thing in morning
- Blocked nose
- Cough or wheeze during the night
- Large adenoids

Solution:

- Children should not eat last thing before bed as food increases breathing.

- A cool bedroom is best (but not cold). High temperatures increase breathing. It is better to have no central heating in a bedroom and to ensure that the duvet or bedclothes are not excessively warm. In addition, an airy unstuffy bedroom is best. Stuffy bedrooms laden with dust mites or animal dander will continuously produce symptoms making it difficult for the child to make any progress. In time, with better breathing, reactions from dust mites and other triggers will be greatly reduced.

- Older children should not sleep on their backs but on the tummy or left hand side. Sleeping on the back is by far the worst position as there is no restriction to breathing. The tummy is the most preferred position, as the weight of the body against the mattress will automatically help the child to breathe less.
- Ensure that the mouth is closed at night.

The relationship between mouth breathing, snoring and sleep apnoea

Snoring is not solely due to the airways being too small but is also because of the breathing volume being too large. Look and listen to the breathing of your child when they are snoring—it is heavy! Snoring comes in two flavours. The more simple form is heavy breathing through the mouth which causes vibrations of the soft palate. This is eliminated when the child learns to breathe through their nose during sleep. The second form is heavy breathing through the nose which creates turbulence. Nasal snoring is eliminated when the child corrects their breathing.

The next stage of progression in sleep related disorders is sleep apnoea. Sleep apnoea is a condition where breathing stops during sleep. If there are more than five apnoeas (breath holds) per hour, it is termed as clinically significant. Small jaws resulting from mouth breathing create small airways leading to an increased incidence of lifelong disorders including sleep apnoea.[1,2]

Nocturnal symptoms arising from sleep apnoea range from snoring, restless sleep, frequent awakenings, apnoeas and sweating. Day time symptoms for adults include fatigue, headaches and cardiac complications. "Unlike adults, few children with obstructive sleep apnoea report excessive daytime sleepiness. Instead, symptoms like behavioural changes, cognitive abnormalities, concentration difficulties and learning difficulties generally occur. Facial growth abnormalities are observed among children with obstructive sleep apnoea and among mouth breathing children, in addition to poor growth due to increased energy expenditure during sleep, hyperactivity and antisocial behaviour, and symptoms of depression, cognitive difficulty and motor dysfunction." [3]

Tens of thousands have effectively applied Buteyko Breathing to help with sleep related problems such as snoring, sleep apnoea and insomnia over the past fifty years.

Closing the mouth at night

The guardian angel

One suggestion which is suitable for children is to have someone watch over them until they become more used to breathing through their nose at night. The role of this person is to gently close their child's mouth when they begin to mouth breathe, or to wake the child up if breathing becomes too heavy. A confirmed insomniac might fill the bill; otherwise, good luck in your search for a guardian angel!

The hat or scarf

Get a hat with a strap that comes under the chin. Cut most of the material from the hat so that there is just enough to keep the structure intact. Cutting away as much material as possible prevents the child from becoming too warm during the night because this would contribute to overbreathing. Get the child to wear the hat to bed and bring the strap under the chin to stop the lower jaw dropping down. A variation on this theme is to wrap a scarf around the child's head and under the chin. Tie it to ensure that the lower jaw is unable to drop down during the night. Both of these suggestions could be consigned to the "off the wall" category by image conscious children.

Paper tape

Paper tape can be bought at most chemists. This option is the most effective and can be worn by older children, teenagers and adults. A good brand is 3M and a suitable size is one inch. Apply it horizontally to cover the mouth. If you are unable to place it in a horizontal position, then place it vertically. Before applying, fold over a tab at either end of the tape to make removal easier in the morning. Wearing the tape at night is imperative to a good night's sleep and will significantly improve energy levels upon waking. In fact, all of the symptoms listed above will be reduced when the mouth is closed at night. If the child is epileptic, feeling nauseous or not comfortable with taping, do not wear the tape.

Some children may possibly, and very reasonably, experience panic at the thought of having their mouth taped. To help overcome this, encourage them to put the tape on their mouth half an hour before going to bed.

This should be enough time to allow them to adjust to using the tape and to overcome any nervousness. For the first few nights, wearing the tape will feel a little strange. It may come off during the night, but at least the child will have spent some hours breathing through their nose. It can also be very helpful for the child to wear the tape around the house during the day as this will help the conversion from a mouth to a nose breather.

Continue to wear the tape until the child has managed to change to breathing through their nose at night. How long this takes will vary from child to child.

MOUTH BREATHING AND DIET

Processed foods

Processed foods are mucus forming and acidic. Mucus is part of the airways defence and traps airbourne particles before they enter the small air sacs within the lungs. If there is excessive production, this thick and sticky secretion can plug and block the airways.

Throughout evolution our diet was 95% alkaline and 5% acidic. Nowadays, the reverse is true; our diet is 95% acidic and 5% alkaline. Acidic food such as dairy, meat, bread, sugar, coffees and teas are all mucus forming and acidify the blood. The body, in an attempt to maintain pH, will stimulate breathing to remove CO_2. (CO_2 is acidic) Alkaline foods are most fruits, vegetables and water. They are breathing friendly foods. (Be careful with citrus fruits as asthmatics can be intolerant to them.)

Food intolerances

Consuming foods to which the child is intolerant will increase their breathing. The most common food intolerances for children with breathing problems such as asthma and blocked nose are chocolate, eggs, milk, cheese, cream, wheat and citrus fruits. When their breathing is correct, the effect from intolerant foods is greatly reduced.

To determine food intolerances, pay attention to what foods cause the child to have symptoms. For example, does the child's nose block, or their chest feel tight or do they produce endless amounts of mucus after they have a glass of milk or an ice-cream? Symptoms may not occur immediately after consuming the intolerant food but could occur the following day.

A good diet consisting of fruits, vegetables, fish, chicken, porridge and water will help breathing. Raw food will help breathing more than cooked.

A poor diet consisting of highly processed, high protein foods and foods to which the child is intolerant to will contribute to big volume breathing. Processed foods which generate greater profit margins are frequently advertised. A rule of thumb is the more they are advertised, the more processed they are.

In addition to eating good food, try to ensure that children and teenagers drink sufficient amounts of water each day. The need for water depends on many factors including outside temperature, amount of physical exercise and diet.

Try to keep an eye on their breathing during eating and drinking as it is common to draw large breaths during this time. Parents have often commented that when their child corrects their breathing, no longer are they breathing noisily or chewing with their mouth open during meal times. It is a normal activity for the child to chew with an open mouth when their nose is blocked.

ESPECIALLY FOR INFANTS

ESPECIALLY FOR INFANTS

Lauren

Overbreathing can occur from a very young age and the precursor may start within the womb. Most modern mothers overbreathe and this increases during pregnancy. As the growing foetus receives its nutrients from the mother, the CO_2 stores in the foetus will also be low.

A baby's breathing rate is significantly higher at about 40 breaths per minute compared with that of an adult who will have ten to twelve breaths per minute.

All babies are obligatory nasal breathers. Although their little mouths can drop open, they still continue to nasal breathe. This can be readily observed when their noses become partially blocked during teething. The babies breathing will get louder as they continue to nasal breathe despite the obstruction. This can create frustration for the child and every now and again they sneeze to free up their nose.

We are born breathing through our nose. We are born diaphragmatically breathing. Our little tummies move in and out with each breath. We are born breathing silently during rest. By the time the child is five years of age, these good habits have often changed into noisy breathing through the mouth and upper chest breathing.

So what causes this change?

As mentioned earlier, the factors that cause overbreathing are related to improved living standards such as overheating of houses, over clothing, over feeding and lack of exercise. Comfort living increases breathing and increased breathing volume is the first step to problems such as asthma, chest infections, rhinitis and hay fever, mouth breathing, ADHD, poor concentration, narrow facial structure, dental problems, snoring and other health related issues.

Switching to mouth breathing

Babies' little mouths can fall open from birth. Even though they nasal breathe, the open mouth during sleep and rest can be the beginning of a lifetime's mouth breathing. As the child grows older, they may have an allergic reaction to dust mites, animal dander, pollen or other airbourne particles which will result in the nose becoming blocked. When the nose gets blocked the natural reaction is for the child to breathe through their mouth. This further disturbs blood gases resulting in a chronically blocked nose.

It is a very good practise to gently press the child's jaw closed whenever it falls open. At the time of writing, my daughter Lauren is three months old. During her first few weeks of life, I gently pressed her lips together any time I saw her mouth open. Sometimes the mouth would only stay closed for a couple of seconds before it would fall open again. However, with continued observation—Lauren has developed the habit of keeping her mouth closed more and more.

Nineteenth Century American painter George Caitlin feared that the traditions of the native American Indians were dying. He therefore spent a year living amongst them so that he could record their customs and habits. His observations are published in a book published in 1870 entitled *Shut Your Mouth and Save your Life*.

One of his observations is as follows; "When I have seen a poor Indian woman in the wilderness, lowering her infant from the breast, and pressing its lips together as it falls asleep … I have said to myself, 'Glorious education! Such a mother deserves to be the nurse of Emperors.'"

Overheating

Caring parents often wrap their babies in excessive layers of clothing and set the temperature within the home too high. When the baby is too hot, they naturally revert to primitive ways of reducing their temperature by breathing faster and heavier. It is worth noting that a baby's metabolism is higher than that of an adult. Therefore, if the adult is comfortable wearing a t-shirt, there is no point wrapping the baby in an under vest, baby grows and other layers. Instead the baby should be dressed in equal to or one less layer than the adult.

Processed foods

As the child grows older, they are bombarded by carefully placed advertisements of processed foods and sugary breakfast cereals which cause the child to breathe heavier.

Lack of physical exercise

Seldom are children encouraged to play outdoors. Nowadays, most forms of entertainment take place in front of the TV or behind a computer screen or hand held game. The same pattern continues as the child grows older. Often I hear parents talk about their teenage sons spending most of the night watching TV and most of their day sleeping. What a waste of the prime of one's life, especially when parents are in a position to do something about it. It is good practise for a parent to encourage their children and teenagers to take part in physical exercise.

Swaddling

Swaddling was a practise carried out by our ancestors. Babies were wrapped up tightly which helped to comfort the child. Physiologically, it makes great sense as it helps to restrict overbreathing by exerting gentle pressure against the chest and tummy of the child. Whenever you have the opportunity, place your infant onto their tummies for a few minutes while they rest on a play mat. Another practise is to place your hands against your child's chest and tummy while they sit on your lap. This will help to calm their breathing.

WHAT TO DO GOING FORWARD

- Use the nose unblocking exercise if your child's nose gets blocked
- Ensure that your child keeps their mouth closed at all times
- Ask your child repeatedly during the day whether their tongue is on the "spot"
- Assist your child to swallow correctly
- If your child is wheezing or coughing, then practise many small breath holds
- When your child has no symptoms, have them practice 10-20 repetitions of Steps each day. (Ideally 6 before breakfast, 6 during the day and 6 before bed.)
- Keep a record of their Steps score and have them try to increase it by 10 each week
- Children should be aware of the concept of reduced breathing and ensure that their breathing is quiet 24/7
- Have them practice reduced breathing

When your child can do 80-100 Steps, do enough repetitions to maintain this figure. For example, after a few weeks the child might be able to maintain 100 steps by just doing 3 repetitions of Steps each day. The Steps score should increase by 10 every week, with a goal of reaching a score of 80 to 100 steps.

An example of a child's progress with Steps is as follows;

Week 1: 26 Steps
Week 2: 35 Steps
Week 3: 47 Steps
Week 4: 60 Steps

Week 5: 69 Steps
Week 6: 80 Steps
Week 7: 80 Steps
Week 8: 70 Steps
Week 9: 80 Steps
Week 10: 100 Steps

It is relatively easy to maintain a high Steps score after it has been reached. This will depend on how aware your child is of their breathing. If for example, your child is not very aware of their breathing and frequently sighs, has noisy breathing, mouth breathes or has large breathing movements throughout the day, then their Steps score will be slow to increase. In this situation it is good practice to continuously remind the child to "ABC" (Always Breathe Correctly).

If you notice that the child's Steps score is decreasing, it is necessary to spend more time practicing the steps during the day. Remember that any time anybody's Steps score drops below 60, then all their symptoms will return.

Another very helpful practise is to perform breath holds during exercise. For example, the child can be holding their breath while walking, on a trampoline, running, riding a horse or whatever physical exercise they like. While doing exercise, the child should try to hold their breath for as long as possible without being stressed. At the end of the breath hold, breathing should be calmed as soon as possible.

CONCLUSION

CONCLUSION

What parent does not want their child to be attractive? What teenager does not want to have a good looking face? What adult if given the choice between an attractive face and an ugly face would choose an ugly face?

Good looking people have many advantages. A cute baby receives more attention than a less attractive. Good looking children receive more praise, social interaction and encouragement.

In films, the good looking person is the hero while the bad guy is often ugly. The intelligent person is good looking and the unintelligent is less attractive. To create further dullness, the unintelligent person is generally portrayed as a mouth breather with the tongue protruding over the lower lip.

Dr Diane Ackerman's book *A Natural History of the Senses*[1] states; "The sad truth is that attractive people do better:

In school, where they receive more help, better grades and less punishment;

At work, where they are rewarded with higher pay, more prestigious jobs and faster promotions;

Finding mates, where they tend to be in control of the relationship and make most of the decisions;

Among strangers, who assume them to be more interesting, honest, virtuous and successful."

Throughout our evolution, social anthropologists regard facial appearance as a determinant in establishing societal rank and role of the individual. "This might explain the influence of good looks on social position, or more significantly, the negative effect of poor facial appearance in this respect."[2]

A good looking face has developed according to how nature intended. The mouth is closed with the tongue in the roof of the mouth, the jaws develop correctly, cheeks are well defined, lips are full and teeth are straight. In other words, straight teeth are the result of correct facial development. The implication of this is that parents who spend thousands of dollars to straighten their child's teeth "are likely to be disappointed, for straight teeth would appear to be the result rather than the cause of an attractive face."[2]

Aesthetics aside, correct breathing volume is essential for good health. While there are hundreds of medical papers and thousands of health professionals advocating it, mainstream medicine and dentistry has overlooked it.

Most dentists and orthodontists do not recommend it despite seeing an increased incidence of dental cavities, crooked teeth and orthodontic relapses among their mouth breathing patients. Child psychiatrists do not advocate correcting breathing volume despite the importance of optimum oxygenation of the brain. Asthma societies and respiratory consultants seldom encourage asthmatics to nasal breathe. The functions of the nose as an effective filter of airbourne allergens and germs is ignored. I attended doctors every couple of months for about twenty years but was never told to breathe through my nose. Only when I learned to nasal breathe and correct my breathing volume did I recover from my asthma, rhinitis, snoring, fatigue and anxiety.

For the most part, children and teenagers with blocked noses are encouraged to take over the counter remedies or are prescribed nasal steroids to unblock their noses. In my experience every single child can be taught to unblock their nose permanently through a combination of breath holds, steps and reduced breathing. In twelve years, I have seen only eight patients who were unable to switch to nasal breathing. This was due to extreme deviation of the septum or severe nasal polyps. (Moderate nasal polyps will shrink when breathing volume is corrected)

Our current healthcare system needs a major shift of consciousness. It is estimated that between 25% and 50% of common conditions including asthma, allergies, rhinitis, fatigue and depression have no known cause.

Treatment of these conditions is dominated by the trillion dollar pharmaceutical industry. Using medication, symptoms are at best managed. Furthermore, long term use of medication creates side effects which are in turn treated with more medications.

Several experts have cited medical mistakes as the third leading cause of death among Americans.[3] Furthermore, it is conservatively estimated that there are over one million medical accidents and adverse reactions to drugs in the UK each year.[4] There is no doubt that something is amiss in current mainstream medicine.

Chronic overbreathing is crying out for attention. It can affect any organ or system with deleterious consequences. While this is well documented in medical journals, little effort is spent on correcting it resulting in millions of children suffering lifelong conditions with significant economic and social costs. Addressing this habit is relatively simple and without side effects.

In the passage of time, I truly believe that the work of both Dr Buteyko and Dr Mew will become universally known, although I don't think the catalyst will be either the medical or dental profession. More than likely, it will be people like you; mothers, fathers, sons and daughters who bring about this change.

A scientific truth does not triumph by convincing its opponents and making them see the light, but rather because its opponents eventually die and a new generation grows up that is familiar with it.

— Max Planck

APPENDIX ONE
Measure breathing volume
The Control Pause

Free video excerpts www.ButeykoKids.com

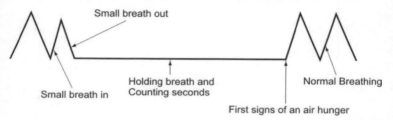

Small breath out

Holding breath and
Counting seconds

Normal Breathing

Small breath in

First signs of an air hunger

Measuring the Control Pause (a)

For this you will need a watch or clock with a second hand.

1. Take a small, silent breath in and a small, silent breath out.
2. Hold your nose with your fingers to prevent air from entering your lungs.
3. Count how many seconds until you feel the first push of your breathing muscles. You might feel the muscles in your tummy (diaphragm) or neck (larynx) jerk as the body senses a need for air. Generally, the first push of the breathing muscles coincide with the first feeling of a need for air.
4. Your inhalation at the end of the breath hold should be no greater than your breathing prior to taking the measurement.
5. Release your nose and breathe in through it. If your breath in is disrupted, then you have held it for too long and have an inaccurate CP.

- You will feel better each time your CP increases by five seconds.
- If your CP does not change, you will not feel better.
- Your CP should increase by three to four seconds each week.
- The most accurate CP is taken first thing after waking.
- Your goal is to have a morning CP of 40 seconds for six months.

APPENDIX TWO
Contact Dr Mew

For a more detailed list of orthodontists, please visit
www.orthotropics.com

In the UK:
Dr John Mew & Dr Mike Mew
www.orthotropics.com
London School of Facial Orthotropics,
Purley Courtyard Clinic,
London
CR8 2NE
England.

Contact Dr Tony O Connor
O Connor Dental Health
Unit 1A Barr-na-Sraide
Main Street
Ballincollig
Co. Cork
Tel: (021)4872600
Email: info@oconnordentalhealth.ie
Web: http://www.oconnordentalhealth.ie/

APPENDIX THREE
Useful contact information

List of qualified Buteyko practitioners

Buteyko practitioner training..www.ButeykoClinic.com

Children's Buteyko DVD...www.ButeykoKids.com

Adult's Buteyko DVD...www.ButeykoDVD.com

Selection of dentists and orthodontists advocating correct swallowing and breathing

Dr Tamara Gray, Texas...www.grayfamilydental.com

Dr William Hang, California...www.facefocused.com

Dr Tony O Connor, Cork, Ireland...............................www.oconnordentalhealth.ie

Dr Hugh McDermott Co Louth, Ireland..Tel: 042 9333679

Dr Ada Murphy Tallaght, Dublin 24...Tel: 01 4513453

Dr Andrew Hatherall...Tel: 01 8476754 or e-mail at
....andrewhatherall@btinternet.com

Myofunctional Therapists

Academy of Orofacial Myofunctional Therapy....................www.myoacademy.net

Barbara Greene California...www.tonguethrust.com

Joy Moeller, California...www.myofunctional-therapy.com

Jeanne Shimizu California...Email: jshimizu@charter.net

Bridget O'Connor, Ireland..www.oconnordentalhealth.ie

Other qualified MyoFunctional therapists with a background in Buteyko can be found from www.ButeykoClinic.com

REFERENCES

Dr Buteyko

1) The American Journal of Medicine; December 1986; Volume 81; p989. Hyperventilation Syndrome and Asthma. (Demeter, Cordasco.)

2) Haughe et al 1980 cited in Multidisiplinary approaches to breathing pattern disorders by Leon Chaitow, Dinah Bradley and Christopher Gilbert

3) When crying it out does not work. By Dr Kathleen Mary Fay. Ref: http://kidsleepdotinfo.synthasite.com/

4) Mouth breathing: adverse effects on facial growth, health academics and behaviour. Gen Dentist 2010 Jan-Feb; 58 (1):18-25; Jefferson Y

Dr Mew

1) Mew, J.R.C. 1986 in Biobloc Therapy published by the Author, Braylsham Castle, Heathfield, U.K

2) Price W. Nutrition and physical degeneration Redlands California

3) Why raise ugly kids? Dr Hal A. Huggins

4) A Black Swan by Mike Mew British Dental Journal 206, 393 (2009) Published online: 25 April 2009 | doi:10.1038/sj.bdj.2009.325

5) Dr John Flutter speaking at BIBH conference 2007

6) Primate experiments on oral respiration. Egil P Harvold. Am J Orthod. Volume 79, issue 4, April 1981, pages 359- 372)

7) Primate experiments on mandibular growth direction. Tomer, Harvold Ep. Am J Orthod 1982 Aug: 82 (2): 114-9

8) Meridith HV: Growth in head width during the first twelve years of life. Pediatrics 12:411-429, 1953

9) Nasal Airway Obstruction In Children and Secondary Dental Deformities SOURCE: UTMB, Dept. of Otolaryngology, Grand Rounds Presentation RESIDENT PHYSICIAN: Carl Schreiner, MD, December 18, 1996

10) Sakuda M Ishizua M. Study of the lip bumper. J Dentist Res. 1970: 49:667

11) Profit. W.R lingual pressure pattern in the transition from tongue thrust to adult swallowing. Arch Oral Biol. 1972:17:555:63

12) Upper airway obstruction and craniofacial morphology. Otolaryngol head neck surgery: 1991 Jun; 104 (6): 881-90)

13) Mental or dental: Dr Raymond Silkman

14) Dr John Flutter: instruction video

15) Malocclusion and upper airway obstruction. Publishes in medicina (Kaunas) 2002; 38 (3): 277- 83)

16) Sixty Seconds interview. Straight talk. Sunday, August 3, 2003
http://sixtyminutes.ninemsn.com.au/article/259072/straight-talk

17) Tourne. The long face syndrome and impairment of the nasopharyngeal airway. Angle Orthod 1990 Fall 60(3) 167-76

18) Nasal Airway Obstruction In Children and Secondary Dental Deformities. RESIDENT PHYSICIAN: Carl Schreiner, MD. December 18, 1996

19) Care of nasal airway to prevent orthodontic problems in children, J Indian Med association 2007 Nov; 105 (11):640,642)

20) Effect of breathing mode and nose ventilation on growth of the facial bones. HNO 1996 May; 4(5):229-34)

21) Skeletal and occlusal characteristics in mouth breathing pre school children. By Mattar SE, Anselmo- Lima WT, Valera FC, Matsumoto MA. Published in J Clin Pediatr Dent 2004 Summer; 28(4): 315-8)

22) Dr Mew. Orthotropics brochure

23) General dentist: Mouth breathing: adverse effects on facial growth, health, academics and behaviour. Jefferson Y, 2010 Jan- Feb; 58 (1):18-25

24) Linder-Aronson S. Adenoids: their effect of the mode of breathing and nasal airflow, and their relationship to characteristics of the facial skeleton and the dentition. Acta Otolaryngology 1970:265 supp.

25) Linder-Aronson S. Adenoid obstruction of the nasopharynx. In: Nasorespiratory function and craniofacial growth. Monograph 9. Craniofacial Growth Series. Ann Arbor: University of Mich. 1979:121-47

26) Linder-Aronson S. Cephalometric radiographs as a means of evaluating the capacity of the nasal and nasopharyngeal airway. Am J Orthod Dentofacial Orthop 1979;76:479-90

27) Linder-Aronson S. mandibular growth following adenoidectomy. Am J Orthod 1986;89:273-84

28) Kerr WJ, McWilliams JS, et al. Mandibular forma and position related to changes mode of breathing—a five year longitudinal study. Angle Orthod 1987;59:91-96

29) Johnston LE Fear and loathing in orthodontics: Notes on the death of theory. Carlson D S. (Ed). The University of Michigan Ann Arbor: Craniofacial Growth Series 23, Center for Human Growth and Development, 1990.

30) Johnston LE. 'Growing Jaws for Fun and Profit.' What doesn't and why. McNamara J A. (Ed). The University of Michigan. Ann Arbor: Craniofacial Growth Series 35, Center for Human Growth and Development, 1999.

31) Mew JRC. Are random controlled trials appropriate for orthodontics? Evid Based Dent 2002; 3: 36.

32) Angle EH. Treatment of malocclusion of the teeth. 7th ed. Philadelphia: S S White Dental Manufacturing Company, 1907.

33) Dispatches, Channel 4, 1999.

34) Independent newspaper.co.uk, Children's dentists at odds in battle of the braces. Sunday, 21 November 1999

35) British Dental Journal 199, 495 - 497 (2005) Published online: 22 October 2005 | doi:10.1038/sj.bdj.4812851)

36) Facial changes in Identical twins treated by different orthodontic techniques. Mew J. World J Orthod. 2007 Summer; 8(2):174-88

37) www.orthotropics.com

Lifestyle factors

1) Tong M, Xia X, Cao E. Cephalometric analysis of the craniofacial bony structures in patients with obstructive sleep apnoea [in Chinese]. Zhonghua Jie He He Hu Xi Za Zhi. 1999;22(6):335-337

2) Hunt CE. Familial small upper airways and sleep-disordered breathing: relationship to idiopathic apparent-life-threatening events. Pediatr Res. 2001;50(1):3-5

3) Mouth breathing children have cephalometric patterns similar to those of adult patients with obstructive sleep apnoea syndrome. Maria Ligia Juliano, Marco Antonio Cardoso Machado, Luciane Bizari Coin de Carvalho, Lucila Bizari Fernandes do Prado, Gilmar Fernandes do Prado. Arquivos de neuro-psiquiatria (Arq Neuropsiquiatr) Vol. 67 Issue 3B Sept 2009:860-5

Conclusion

1) Ackerman, D. A natural history of the senses. Cornell University. 1990.

2) Mew, J.R.C. 1986 in Biobloc Therapy published by the Author, Braylsham Castle, Heathfield, U.K

3) Starfield B (2000) Is US health really the best in the world? Journal of the American medical association 284(4): 483-5; Null G, Dean C, (2003) Death by Medicine. New York. Nutrition Institute of America

4) National Audit Office Report (3 November 2005) Available from: www.nao.org.uk/publications/nao_reports/05-06/0506456.pdf

BOOK THREE

ESPECIALLY FOR CHILDREN

**ButeykoKids Always
Breathe Correctly**

This is Michael. He would love to run and play with his friends, but he cannot because he breathes through his mouth.

This causes him to cough and wheeze, and to become breathless. It also makes him tired and slows him down.

One day he sees a sign for the summer's sports day.

He makes a wish to be able to play in the games.

His wish is, "I wish I could run a race this summer."

Later on that night just before Michael falls asleep,
Argo the wizard appears.

He whispers into Michael's ear: "If you want your wish
to come true....you must play the ABC Game."
And the **ABC Game** is....
Always
Breathe
Correctly

This is very helpful for your sports, your growing face,
your teeth and your brains!

The next morning, Michael awakes and thinks it was all just a dream, but Argo the wizard appears again, and this time Michael is awake. He reminds Michael that he did not play the **ABC Game** while he was sleeping.

Michael does not know how to breathe correctly so the wizard explains it to him like this:

The ABC Game:

Part 1 is **Breathe through your nose both day and night with your tongue on the "spot."**

Part 2 is **Practice an exercise called Steps each day.**

Part 3 is **Always breathe gently and calmly like a little mouse.**

Part 1 of the **ABC Game** is to breathe through your nose all the time.

Michael tried to breathe through his nose all that day but it kept getting blocked and that made it difficult.

Then Argo the wizard appears. He whispers into Michael's ear the secret of how to unblock his nose.

You can try this too. Here's how:

- Sit down.

- Take a small breath in through your nose.

- This breath should make no noise.

- Breathe out through your nose.

- Then hold your nose with your fingers so that the air cannot come in or go out.

- Gently nod your head up and down.

- Do this for as long as you can.

- When you need to breathe in, then breathe in through your nose only and try not to let the air sneak in through your mouth.

- Calm your breathing as quickly as possible.

- Wait about half a minute and practice this again. Your nose will be unblocked by the third attempt. If it is not; practice this again until your nose is unblocked.

- If your nose gets blocked again; practise the exercise again.

Argo tells Michael that it is very important to breathe through the nose. Your nose, he says, stops dirty air from coming in and nibbling at the inside of your body. He also explains that the nose warms and cleans the air for us.

We all know that:

- We use our **Eyes** for seeing
- We use our **Ears** for listening
- We use our **Mouth** for talking, eating and drinking
- While we use our **Nose** for smelling and breathing

So, breathe only through your nose because that is why we all have noses!

Argo tells Michael:

"Michael, I am going to let you know of another secret. It is from a famous dentist called Dr Mew.

If you breathe through your mouth, your face will grow long and narrow and your teeth will be crooked. Look at the boy who kept his mouth open as a child."

"Michael, if you breathe through your nose and your tongue rests in the roof of your mouth, you will grow the perfect face and have straight teeth."

To place your tongue on the correct "spot"

Make the "N" sound. Your tongue will rest behind the top front teeth. Keep the tip of your tongue there. Now gently move your tongue up into the roof of your mouth. Great, this is the "spot". Try to keep your tongue on the "spot" at all times.

Always ask yourself these questions:

Is my mouth closed?

Is my tongue on the "spot"?

To practice swallowing correctly;

For this exercise, you need an ice cream wafer. Break off a piece about the size of a quarter, 10p or a one Euro coin. Chew until you can make a ball out of it. Shape your tongue into a hollow and place the ball near the front.

Place the tip of your tongue on the "N spot" and close your teeth, pressing your tongue firmly against the skin of the roof of your mouth and not the teeth.

Then swallow, sucking at the same time. The teeth should bite together. The lips should be held apart in a big grin. This helps the back of the tongue rise up and stops the lips being involved in the swallow. With the lips apart, an adult can also check how you did. With a correct swallow there is no sign of movement from the outside of your face.

Use a mirror afterwards to see that none of the ice cream wafer is left on your tongue.

If you don't have a wafer, you can use a small piece of bread.

From now on, every time you swallow, make sure that your tongue is in the roof of your mouth.

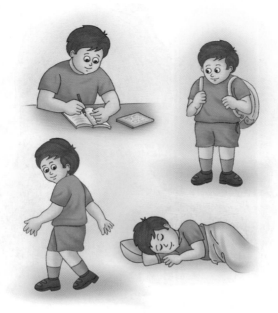

Each day, if Michael has his mouth open, Argo appears and whispers "**ABC**" into his ear...

- During physical exercise — **ABC**

- During walking — **ABC**

- At School — **ABC**

- Watching TV — **ABC**

- Doing homework — **ABC**

- Playing outdoors — **ABC**

- While asleep — **ABC**

After a few days, Argo the wizard is very happy because Michael does not breathe through his mouth at all. Michael also keeps his tongue on the "spot." The wizard decides to teach Michael Part 2 of ABC, a game called Steps.

To play one set of Steps:

- Take a small breath in through your nose

- Breathe a small breath out through your nose

- Hold your nose so that air does not enter or escape

- Walk as many steps as you can while holding your breath

- When you really need to breathe in, let go of your nose and breathe in through your nose

- Calm your breathing as quickly as possible

	David's steps	One minute rest	David's steps	One minute rest	David's steps	One minute rest	David's steps	One minute rest	David's steps	One minute rest	David's steps
Line 1	7	☺	8	☺	8	☺	9	☺	11	☺	12
Line 2	10	☺	11	☺	8	☺	12	☺	15	☺	13

Michael does two lines of Steps each day. Each line contains six sets of Steps. After doing one set of Steps, he rests for about one minute. He then does the next set of Steps and rests for one minute until he has completed all six.

Each time he does the Steps he tries to get a higher number than the one before. Sometimes he can, sometimes he cannot.

Above is a chart of Michael's Steps on his first day.

Steps are fun...just like ABC. You can also play the Game of Steps. Be sure to read the **Note of Caution** before commencing steps.

Argo has drawn a table at the back of the book especially for you to complete.

Each day Argo the wizard appears to Michael and whispers "ABC." Hearing this, Michael repeats his Steps exercises.

Every time Michael forgets to keep his mouth closed or his tongue on the "spot," Argo appears to Michael and says: **"Remember to ABC"**

Michael is able to do more and more Steps each week. The wise wizard feels that his student is making very good progress. Michael is now ready to hear part three of the ABC Game. Here it is:

BIG BREATHING CAUSES THE MOUTH TO BE OPEN, A BLOCKED NOSE, COUGHING, WHEEZING AND BREATHLESSNESS

Michael knows he is big breathing anytime he can **hear** his breathing while sitting down, or while asleep. Michael also knows he is big breathing if his **mouth** is **open**.

Argo blows a big amount of air onto Michael's hand. He tells Michael that this is big breathing. A dinosaur breathes the same way, he says.

Argo then blows a tiny amount of air onto Michael's hand so that Michael can feel very little air. He tells Michael that this is correct breathing, and it's just like the breathing of a little mouse.

Argo asks Michael to breathe like a little mouse, breathing quietly all the time.

Argo tells Michael the secret of how to breathe like a little mouse. Michael is to breathe like a little mouse anytime **he can HEAR** himself breathe.

To do this:

- Place your finger under your nose
- Try to feel the warm air on your finger
- Now breathe very little so that you cannot feel the amount of warm air on your finger

Michael pretends that he is a little white mouse. He tries to breathe very quietly and gently. There is no sound at all from Michael's breathing.

Argo the wizard has one final word of wisdom for Michael.

"Michael", he says, "if you ever see pollution or dirty air, try not to let it into your body."

The secret is:

- Breathe in

- Breathe out

- Hold your breath and walk away from the dirty air

Argo wants to tell his secret to every boy and girl. He has written this especially for you.

He says:

"**ABC** each day.

Keep your **mouth closed** all the time during the day and night.

Place your tongue on **the spot**.

Practise two lines of **Steps** each day.

Any time you can hear your own breathing, breathe like a **little mouse**.

This is the **ABC**."

The summer sports day comes and Michael signs up for the race.

The other children laugh and make fun of Michael because they all think he cannot run.

Michael is afraid that he will be too slow so he runs off.

But Argo the wizard appears and whispers "**ABC**" to Michael. He tells Michael to take part in the race.

He says "Michael, you can be very fast if you can do more than eighty steps."

The higher the number of steps the better.

Michael has practised two rows of Steps every day.

After a couple of months Michael can now walk 80 steps each time. He is now ready to race.

Below is his table of Steps on the last day before the race:

	David's steps	One minute rest	David's steps	One minute rest	David's steps	One minute rest	David's steps	One minute rest	David's steps	One minute rest	David's steps
Line 1	80	☺	81	☺	82	☺	80	☺	85	☺	82
Line 2	83	☺	82	☺	80	☺	85	☺	81	☺	86

Michael runs in the race.

He is halfway to the finish line.

All the other boys and girls are running as fast as they can.

Michael wins the race. He is faster than all the other boys and girls.

Everybody cheers with delight.

Argo the wizard is so happy. Michael is great at running.

"HOW DID HE DO IT?" they ask

Michael tells them: "I did it because of the **ABC Game**."

ALWAYS BREATHE CORRECTLY.

- Breathe through your nose all the time.
- Place your tongue on the "spot."
- Practice Steps twice per day. The goal is to reach eighty steps.
- Any time you can hear yourself breathing, breathe quietly and gently just like a little mouse.

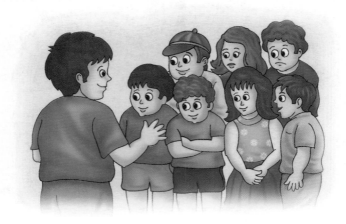

Michael tells them that **ABC**:

- Stops coughing and wheezing
- Stops breathlessness
- Helps sports
- Helps grow the perfect face
- Helps teeth and gums because the mouth is closed

Michael can now play, run, jog, skip, swim and do anything that he wants to do...

Thanks to the ABC.

Steps Record

Date	My Steps	One Minute Rest	My Steps	One Minute Rest	My Steps	One Minute Rest	My Steps	One Minute Rest	My Steps	One Minute Rest	My Steps

Photocopy this page and start recording your progress.
Rest for one minute between each repetition of steps.
Two rows of steps per day with at least two hours rest
in between each line. Steps should be practised on an
empty tummy.

A Note of Caution

Steps exercises are specifically aimed towards children and teenagers. While steps are a perfectly safe exercise, (similar to swimming underwater) it can involve an element of risk for some children with particular illnesses or susceptibilities.

Please note the following in particular:

- Do not commence steps if you have any of the following conditions: diabetes; severe asthma; epilepsy; schizophrenia; sickle cell anaemia; arterial aneurysm; any heart problems; uncontrolled hyperthyroidism; a known brain tumour or kidney disease.

- If you experience an exacerbation of your symptoms, then you are not doing the exercises correctly and you should stop until you establish that you can do them correctly. If the child is having breathing difficulty, then do not do steps. Steps exercises are only to be practised when no symptoms are present.

What to expect

Roughly two thirds of those who apply steps will experience a cleansing reaction within the first two weeks. Cleansing reactions are indicative of the powerful physiological change which the body undergoes.